Arranged for piano/voice/guitar. Full lyrics/guitar chord boxes.

THE 50 TOP SINGLES OF ALL-TIME

Wise Publications
London / New York / Paris / Sydney / Copenhagen / Madrid

Exclusive Distributors:
Music Sales Limited
8/9 Frith Street, London W1V 5TZ, England.
Music Sales Pty Limited
120 Rothschild Avenue, Rosebery, NSW 2018, Australia.

Order No. AM949531
ISBN 0-7119-7373-3
This book © Copyright 1999 by Wise Publications.

Compiled by Peter Evans.
Cover design by Michael Bell Design.
Photographs courtesy of
London Features International / Rex Features /
Pictorial Press / All Action.
Printed and bound in Malta by Interprint Limited

Your Guarantee of Quality
As publishers, we strive to produce every book to
the highest commercial standards.
This book has been carefully designed to minimise awkward page turns
and to make playing from it a real pleasure.
Particular care has been given to specifying acid-free,
neutral-sized paper made from pulps which have not been elemental chlorine bleached.
This pulp is from farmed sustainable forests and was
produced with special regard for the environment.
Throughout, the printing and binding have been planned to ensure a sturdy,
attractive publication which should give years of enjoyment.
If your copy fails to meet our high standards, please inform us
and we will gladly replace it.

Music Sales' complete catalogue describes thousands of
titles and is available in full colour sections by
subject, direct from Music Sales Limited.
Please state your areas of interest and send a
cheque/postal order for £1.50 for postage to:
Music Sales Limited, Newmarket Road, Bury St. Edmunds, Suffolk IP33 3YB.

A Woman In Love

Words & Music by Barry Gibb & Robin Gibb

you know we nev-er know why. ———
live in each oth-er's heart.

The road is nar-row and long ———
We may be o-ceans a-way ———

when eyes meet eyes ——— and the feel-ing is strong. ———
you feel my love ——— I hear what you say. ———

I turn a-way from the wall. ——— I stum-ble and fall, ——— but I give you it all. ———
The truth is ev-er a lie. ——— I stum-ble and fall, ——— but I give you it all. ———

I am a wom-an in love ——— and I'd do an-y-thing ———

to get you in-to my world, ——— and hold you with-in. ——— It's a

what a wom-an can do.____ It's a right____ I de-

-fend o-ver and o-ver a-gain.

I am a wom-an in love,____ and I'd do an-y-thing____ to get you in-to my world,

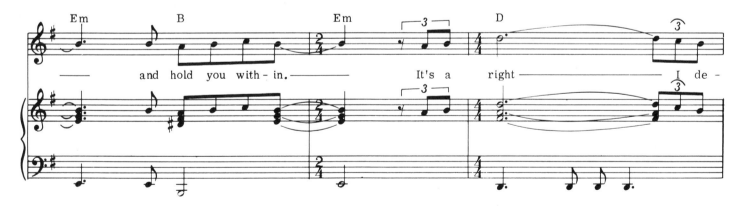

and hold you with-in.____ It's a right____ I de-

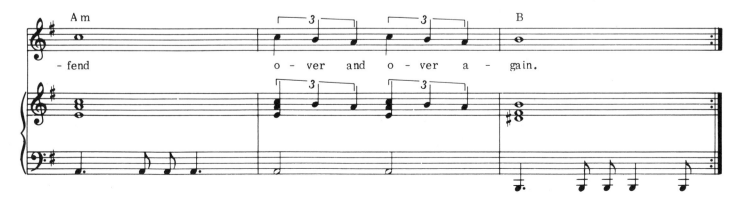

-fend o-ver and o-ver a-gain.

A Whiter Shade Of Pale

Words & Music by Keith Reid & Gary Brooker

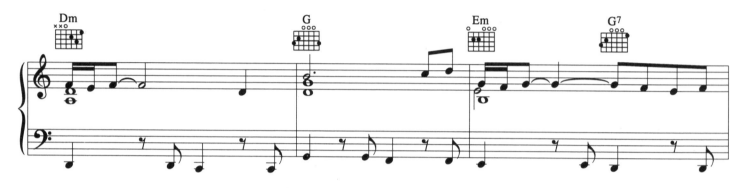

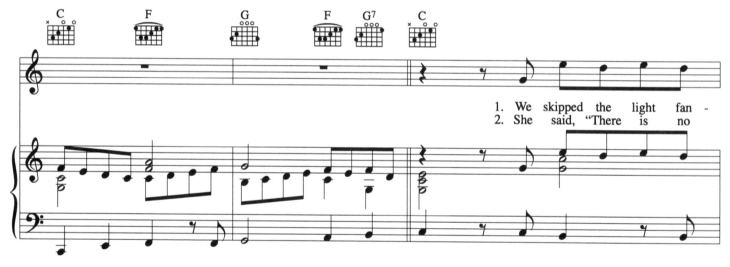

1. We skipped the light fan no
2. She said, "There is no

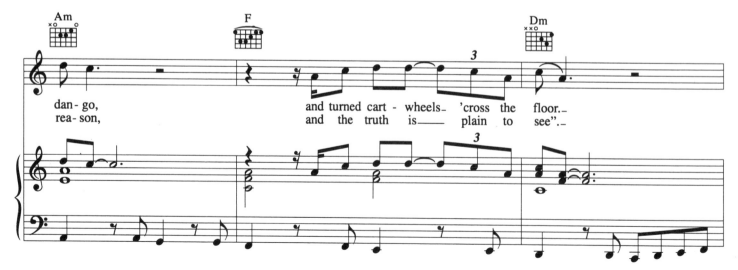

dan - go,
rea - son,

and turned cart - wheels_ 'cross the floor._
and the truth is___ plain to see".–

I was feel - ing kind of sea - sick,
But I wan - dered through my play - ing cards

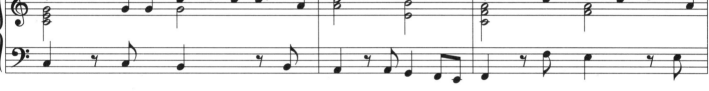

but the crowd called out for more,
and would not let her be.

the room was hum - ming
One of six - teen ves - tal

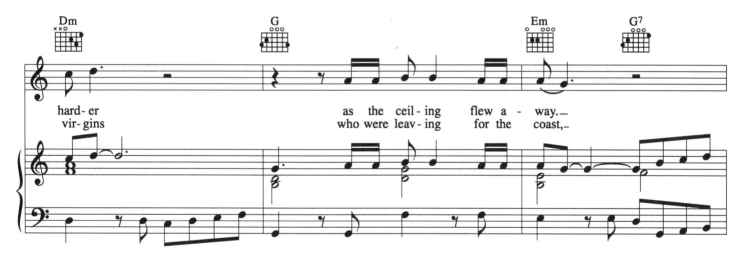

hard - er
vir - gins

as the ceil - ing flew a - way.
who were leav - ing for the coast,

When we called out for an - oth - er drink
and al - tho' my eyes were op - en

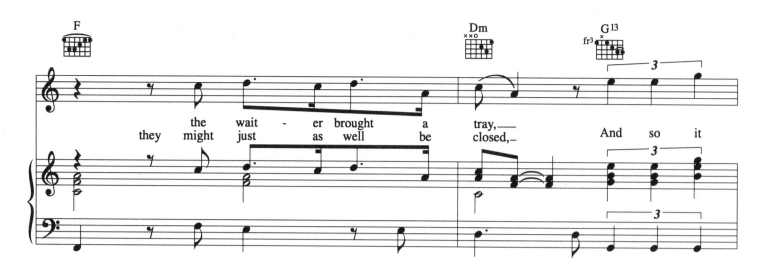

they the might wait just - er as brought well a be tray,— closed,— And so it

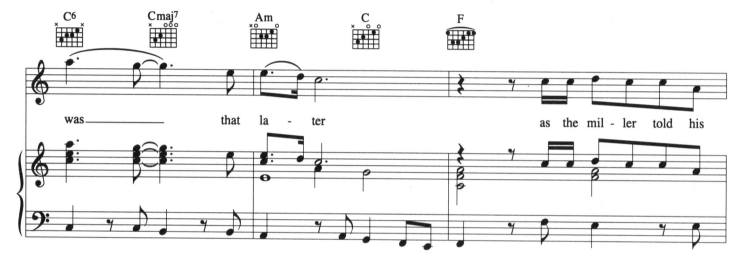

was—————— that la - ter as the mil - ler told his

tale,— that her face at first just ghost- ly, turned a

whit - er——— shade of pale.——— pale.———

Against All Odds
(Take A Look At Me Now)

Words & Music by Phil Collins

Slow rock

N.C.

1. How can I just let you walk a-way,   just let you
(Verses 2 & 3 see block lyric)

leave with-out a trace? When I stand here tak-ing ev-'ry breath with you;

ooh, you're the on-ly one who real-ly knew me at all.

Verse 2:
How can you just walk away from me
When all I can do is watch you leave?
'Cause we shared the laughter and the pain
And even shared the tears.
You're the only one who really knew me at all.

Verse 3:
I wish I could just make you turn around
Turn around and see me cry.
There's so much I need to say to you
So many reasons why.
You're the only one who really knew me at all.

All You Need Is Love

Words & Music by John Lennon & Paul McCartney

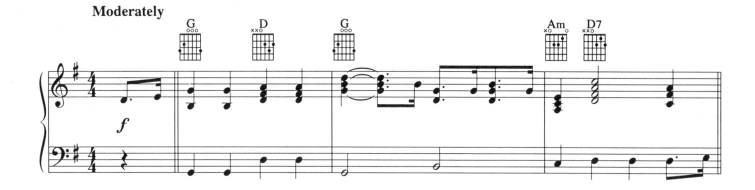

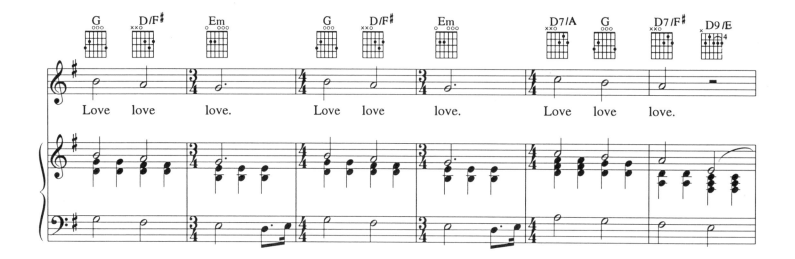

Love love love. Love love love. Love love love.

1. There's no-thing you can do that can't be done. ___
2. There's no-thing you can make that can't be made. ___
3. There's no-thing you can know that is-n't known. ___

No-thing you can sing that can't be sung. ____
No-one you can save that can't be saved. ____
No-thing you can see that is-n't shown. ____

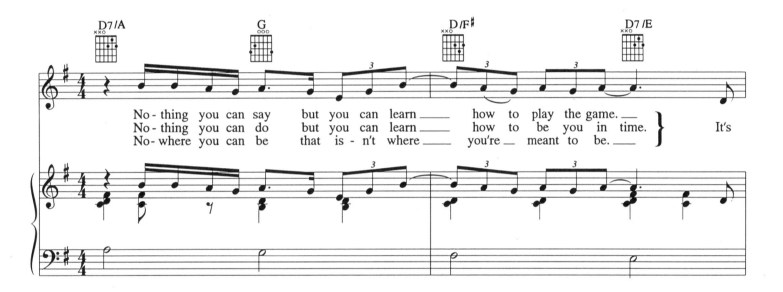

No-thing you can say but you can learn ____ how to play the game. ____
No-thing you can do but you can learn ____ how to be you in time. ____
No-where you can be that is-n't where ____ you're ____ meant to be. ____
It's

ea - sy.
All you need is love, ____

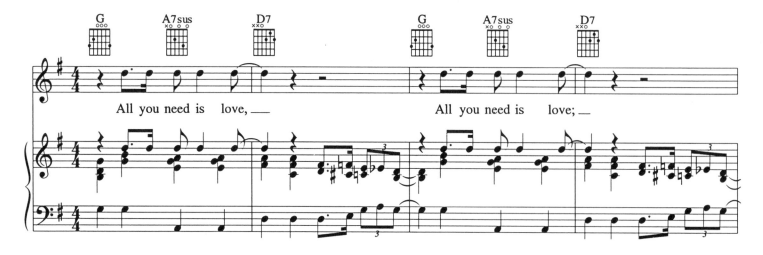

All Right Now

Words & Music by Paul Rodgers & Andy Fraser

19

Angels

Words & Music by Robbie Williams & Guy Chambers

♩ = 76

I sit and wait, _____ does an an- -gel con-tem-plate _____ my fate, _____ and do they know the pla-ces where we go when we're grey and old _____ 'cos I have been _____ told that sal-va- -tion lets their wings

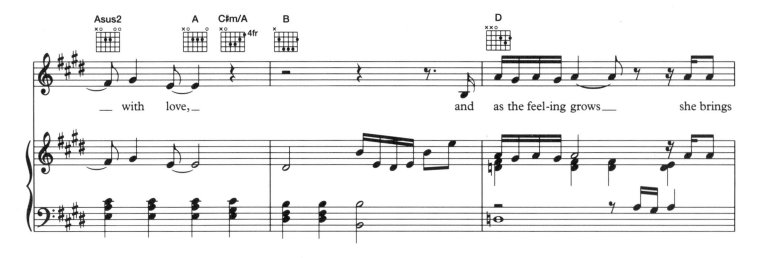

with love, ___ and as the feel-ing grows ___ she brings

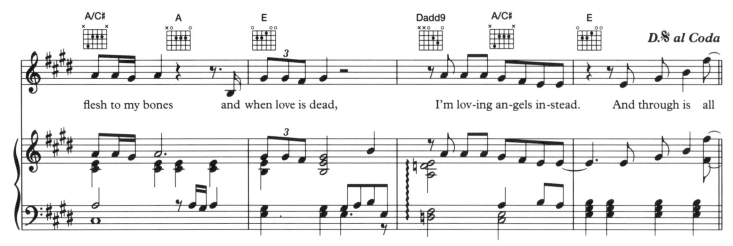

flesh to my bones and when love is dead, I'm lov-ing an-gels in-stead. And through is all

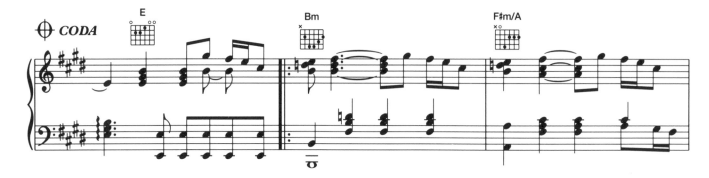

Another Day In Paradise

Words & Music by Phil Collins

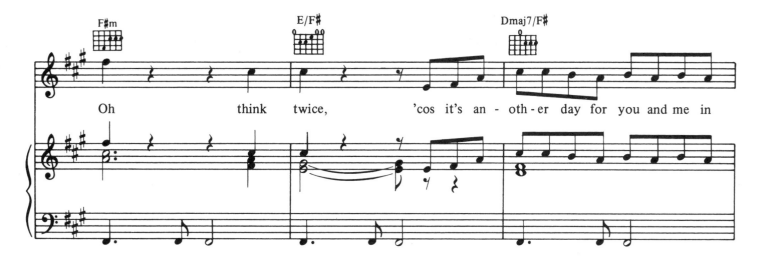

Oh think twice, 'cos it's an-oth-er day for you and me in

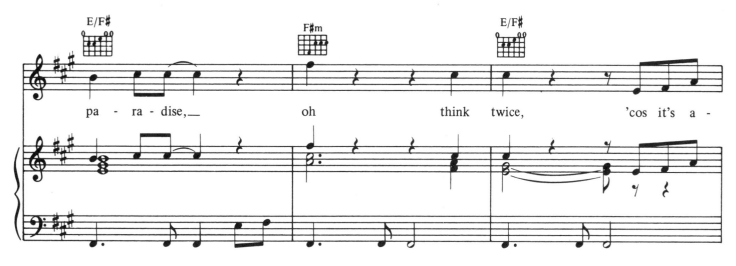

pa-ra-dise,__ oh think twice, 'cos it's a-

no-ther day for you,__ you and me in pa-ra-dise.__

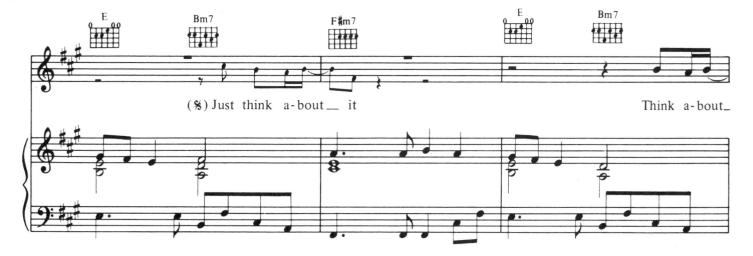

(%) Just think a-bout__ it Think a-bout__

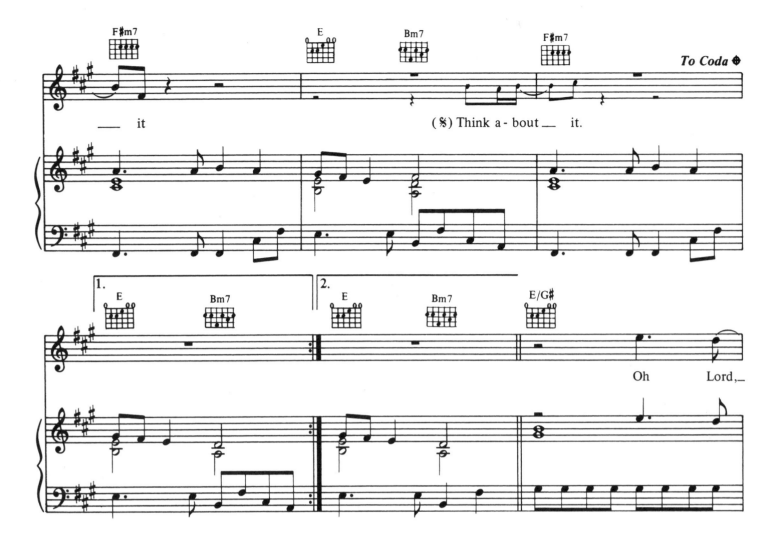

To Coda ⊕

__ it   (%) Think a - bout __ it.

Oh   Lord,__

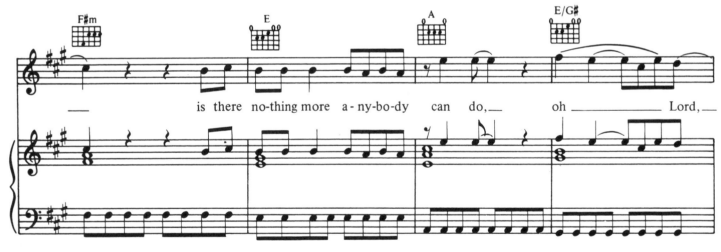

is there no-thing more a-ny-bo-dy can do,__ oh _____ Lord,__

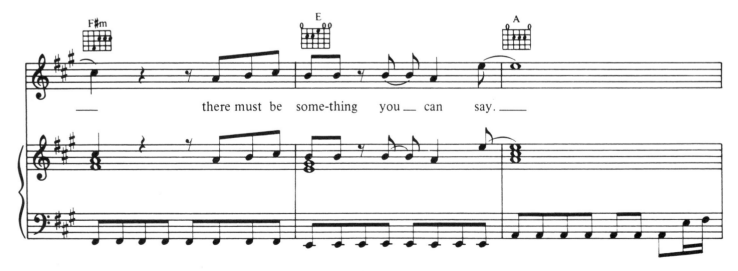

there must be some-thing you __ can say. __

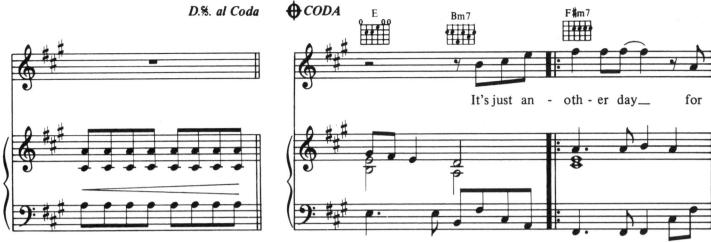

VERSE 2:
He walks on, doesn't look back,
He pretends he can't hear her,
Starts to whistle as he crosses the street,
Seems embarrased to be there.

VERSE 3:
She calls out to the man on the street,
He can see she's been crying,
She's got blisters on the soles of her feet,
She can't walk, but she's trying.

VERSE 4: (𝄋)
You can tell from the lines on her face,
You can see that she's been there,
Probably been moved on from every place,
'Cos she didn't fit in there.

29

Brown Eyed Girl

Words & Music by Van Morrison

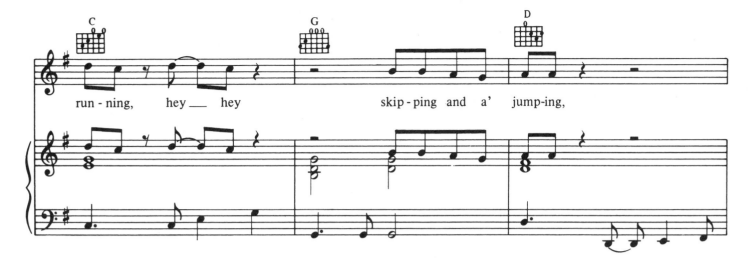

run - ning, hey __ hey ... skip-ping and a' jump-ing,

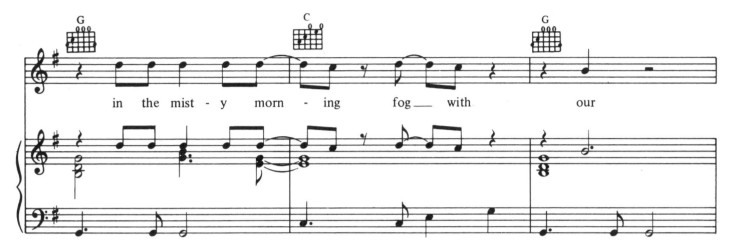

in the mist - y morn - ing fog __ with ... our

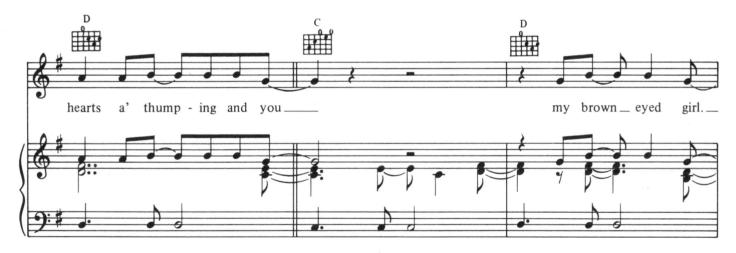

hearts a' thump - ing and you __ ... my brown __ eyed girl. __

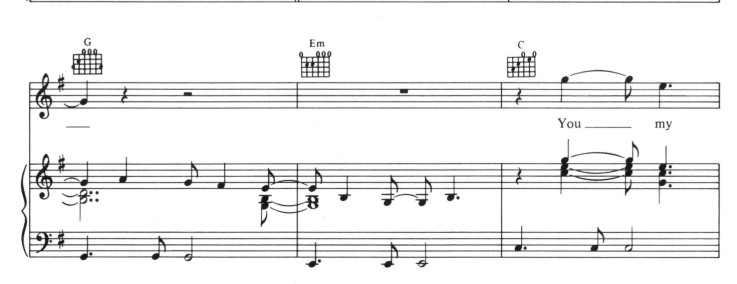

__ ... You __ my

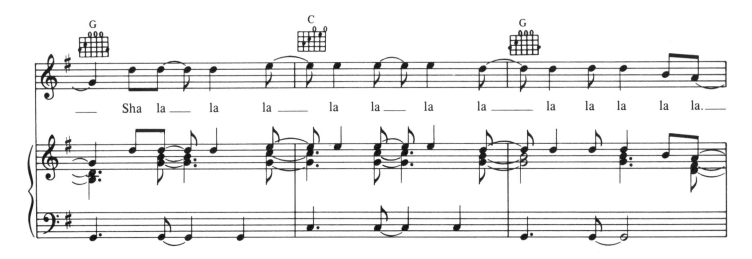

la la la la la   la te da.

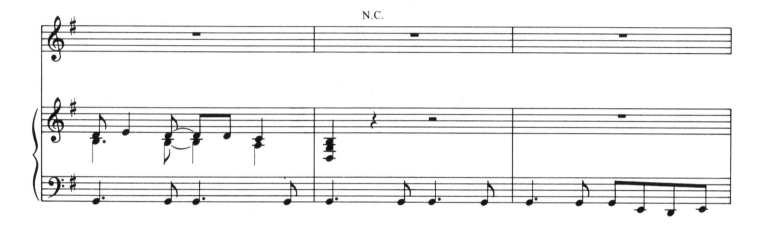

VERSE 2:
Whatever happened
To Tuesday and so slow
Going down the old mine
With a transistor radio
Standing in the sunlight laughing
Hiding behind a rainbow's wall
Slipping and a' sliding
All along the waterfall
With you, my brown eyed girl
You, my brown eyed girl.

VERSE 3:
So hard to find my way
Now that I'm all on my own
I saw you just the other day
My, how you have grown
Cast my memory back there Lord
Sometimes I'm overcome thinkin' 'bout it
Laughing and a' running, hey hey
Behind the stadium
With you, my brown eyed girl
You, my brown eyed girl.

Candle In The Wind

Words & Music by Elton John & Bernie Taupin

1. Good-bye Nor - ma Jean _____ though I nev - er knew you at all _____
2. Lone - li - ness _____ was tough _____ the tough-est role you ev - er played Hol - ly

_____ you had _____ the grace to hold your - self _____ while those a - round _____ you crawled
-wood cre - at - ed a _____ su - per star _____ and pain was the price you paid

They crawled out of the wood-work _____ and they whis-pered
ev - en when you died _____ Oh the

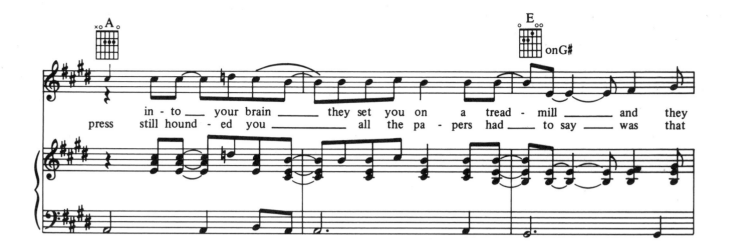

in - to ___ your brain ___ they set you on a tread-mill ___ and they
press still hound - ed you ___ all the pa - pers had ___ to say ___ was that

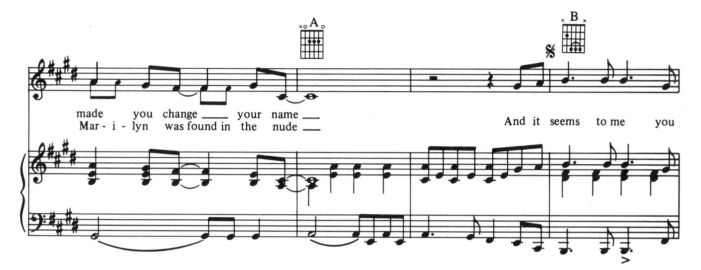

made you change ___ your name ___
Mar - i - lyn was found in the nude ___ And it seems to me you

lived your life ___ like a can - dle in ___ the wind ___ Nev - er

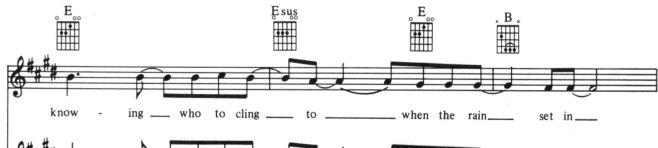

know - ing ___ who to cling ___ to ___ when the rain ___ set in ___

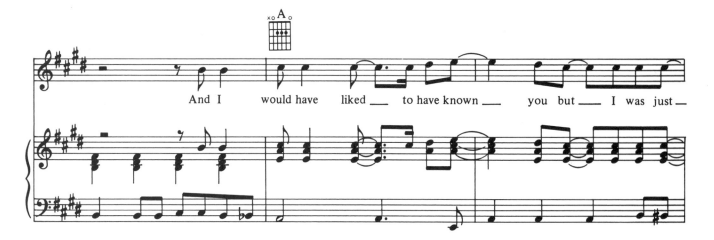

And I would have liked __ to have known __ you but __ I was just __

__ a kid __ Your can-dle had burned __ out long __ be-fore __ your

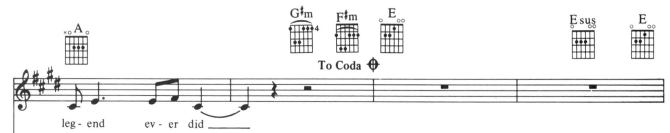

To Coda

leg-end ev-er did __

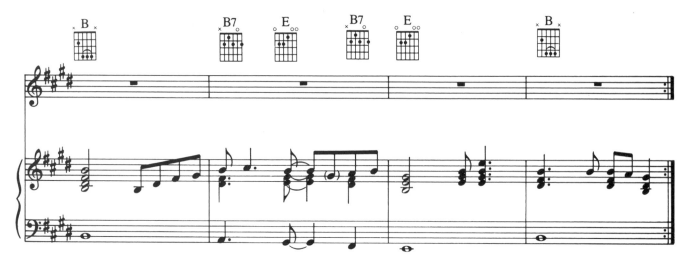

Good-bye Nor - ma Jean _____ though I nev - er knew you at all _____
Good-bye Nor - me Jean _____ from the young man in the twen - ty sec - ond row _____

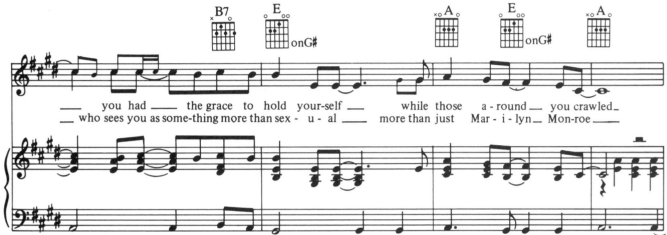

_____ you had _____ the grace to hold your-self _____ while those a - round _____ you crawled _____
_____ who sees you as some-thing more than sex - u - al _____ more than just Mar - i - lyn Mon - roe _____

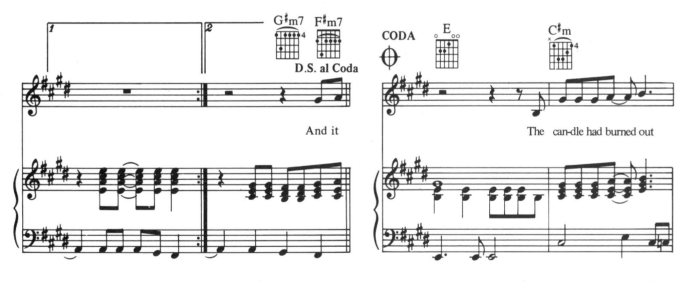

D.S. al Coda

And it

CODA

The can-dle had burned out

long _____ be - fore _____ your leg - end ev - er did. _____

Careless Whisper

Words & Music by George Michael & Andrew Ridgeley

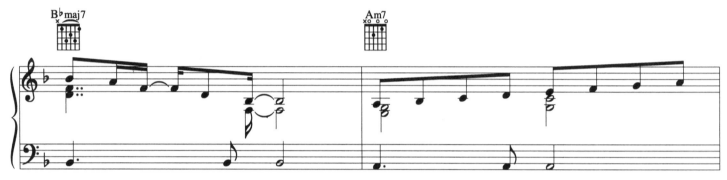

I feel   so —— un - sure ——
Time can   nev - er   mend ——
To - night the mu - sic seems so loud, — I

way I dance _ with you. _____

way I dance _ with you, oh. _____

D.%.al Coda

⊕ Coda

way I dance _ with you. _____

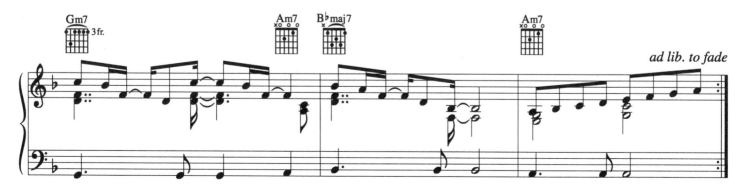

ad lib. to fade

Bridge Over Troubled Water

Words & Music by Paul Simon

Moderate, not too fast, like a spiritual

Rubato

When you're wea - ry, __ feel - ing _____ small,
down and out, __ When you're on the street,

When tears are in your eyes, __ I'll dry them _ all;
When eve - ning falls so hard __ I will com - fort _ you.

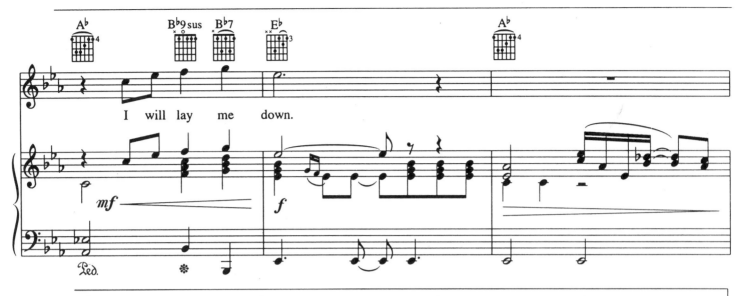

I will lay me down.

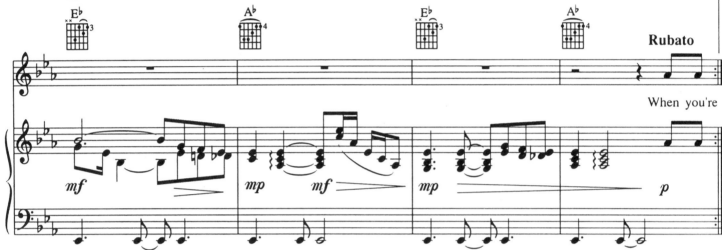

When you're

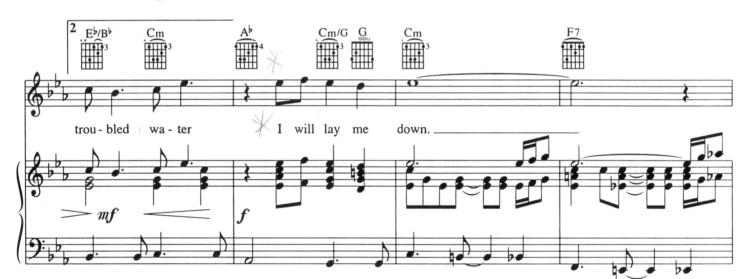

trou-bled wa-ter I will lay me down.

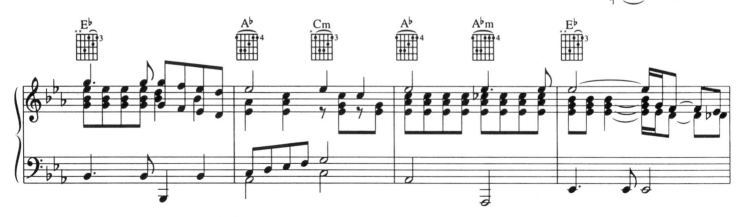

Dancing Queen

Words & Music by Benny Andersson, Stig Anderson & Bjorn Ulvaeus

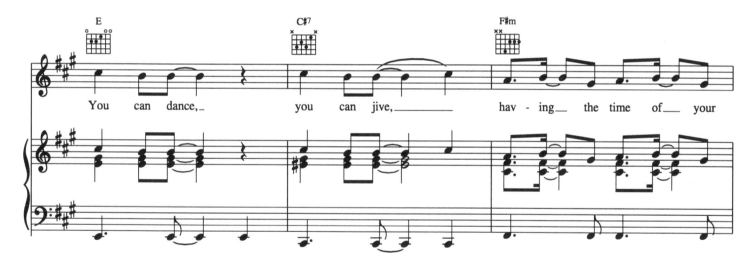

You can dance, _ you can jive, _____ hav - ing _ the time of _ your

life. ___ Oh, _____ see that _ girl, ___ watch that _ scene, _ dig in the

danc - ing__ queen.

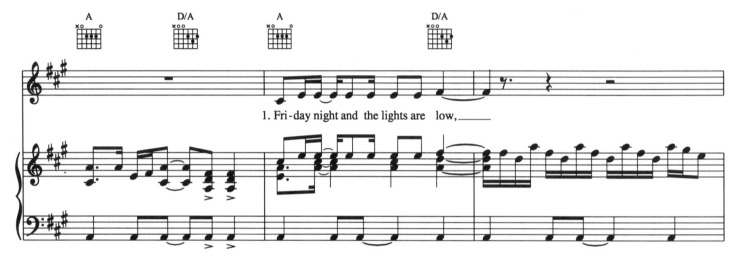

1. Fri-day night and the lights are low,_____

look-ing out__ for a place to go,_____ Oh,_____ where they play the right mu-sic,

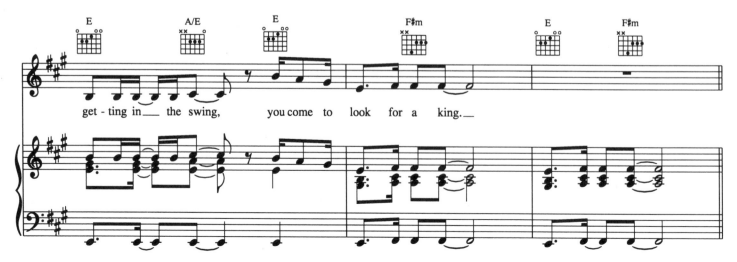

get - ting in__ the swing, you come to look for a king.__

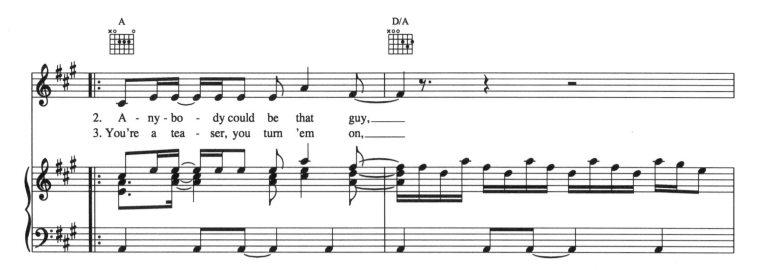

2. A - ny - bo - dy could be that guy,_____
3. You're a tea - ser, you turn 'em on,_____

night is young and the mu - sic's high,
leave 'em burn - ing and then you're gone,

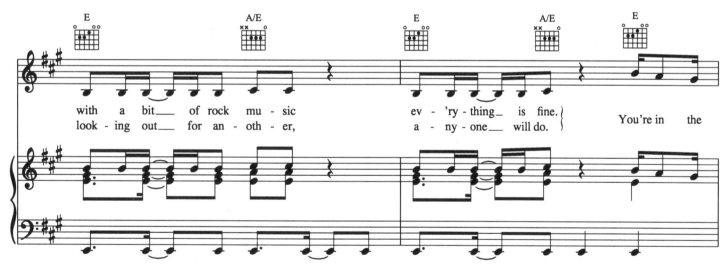

with a bit___ of rock mu - sic ev - 'ry - thing___ is fine.
look - ing out___ for an - oth - er, a - ny - one___ will do. ⎫
⎬ You're in the
⎭

mood for a dance,_ and when you get the___ chance,_____

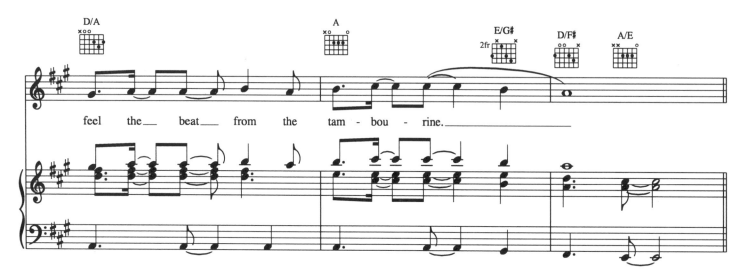

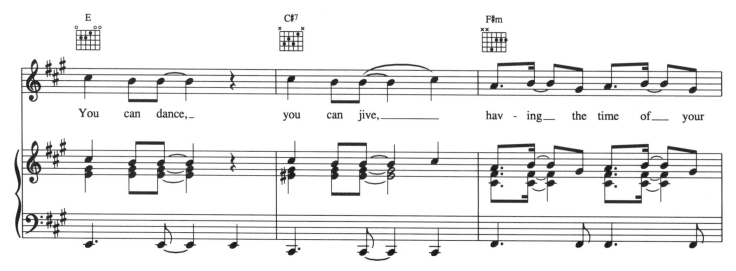

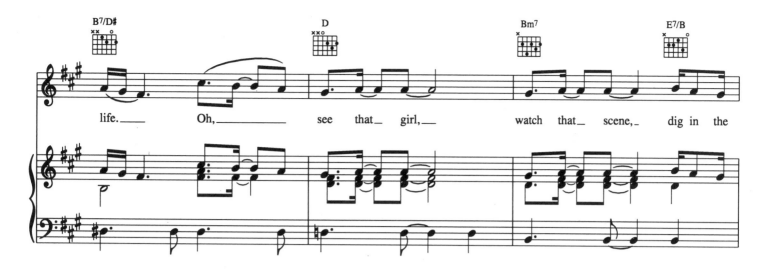

life.____ Oh,_____ see that_ girl,__ watch that_ scene,_ dig in the

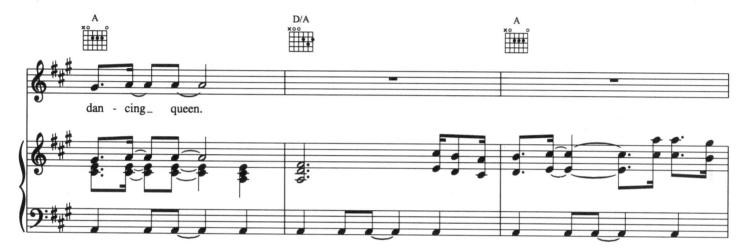

dan - cing_ queen.

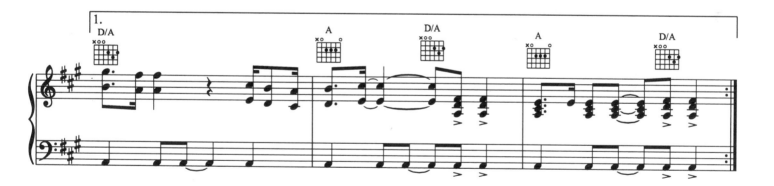

1.

2.

Dig in the dan - cing queen.

repeat and fade

Every Breath You Take

Words & Music by Sting

Medium rock

Ev - 'ry breath you — take   ev - 'ry move you —

make,   ev - 'ry bond — you break   ev - 'ry step — you take

I'll be watch-ing you. Ev-'ry sin-gle— day

ev - 'ry word you— say, ev-'ry game— you play

ev - 'ry night— you stay, I'll be watch-ing you.

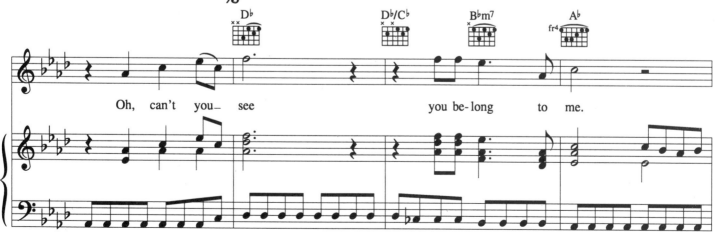

Oh, can't you— see you be-long to me.

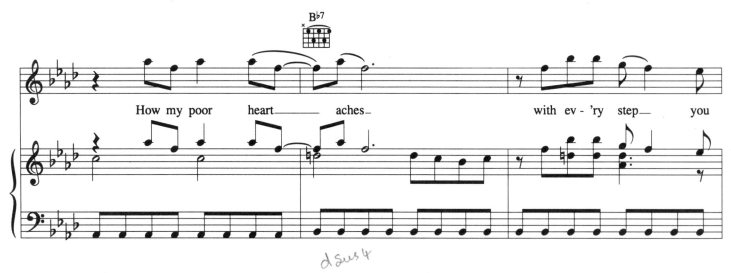

How my poor heart_____ aches_____ with ev-'ry step_____ you

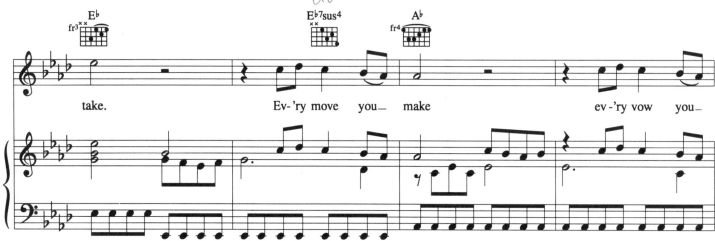

take. Ev-'ry move you_____ make ev-'ry vow you_____

break, ev-'ry smile_____ you fake ev-'ry claim_____ you stake,

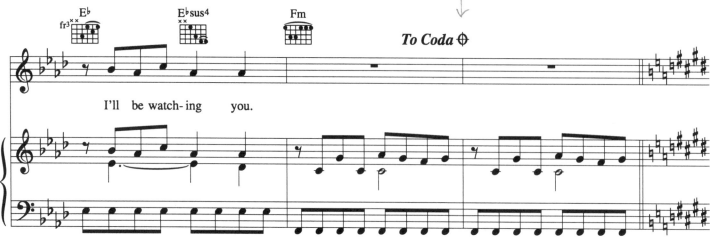

To Coda ⊕

I'll be watch-ing you.

Since you've gone,— I been lost— with - out— a trace, I dream at night I can on -

- ly see— your face, I look a-round but it's you I can't— re-place, I feel so cold and I

long for your— em-brace. I keep cry - ing ba - by ba - by please.—

2° only

D.%. al Coda ✛ Coda

Oh can't you—

Ev-'ry move— you make ev-'ry step— you take,

I'll be watch-ing you.

Repeat ad lib. to fade

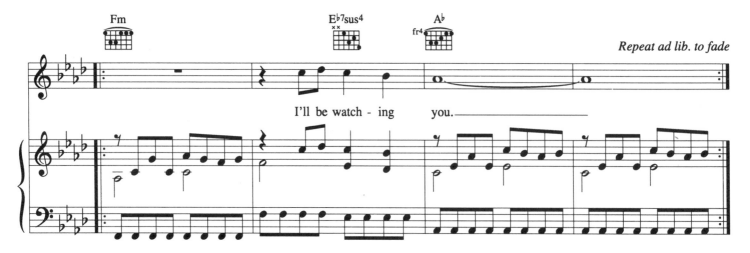

I'll be watch-ing you.—

Good Vibrations

Words & Music by Brian Wilson & Mike Love

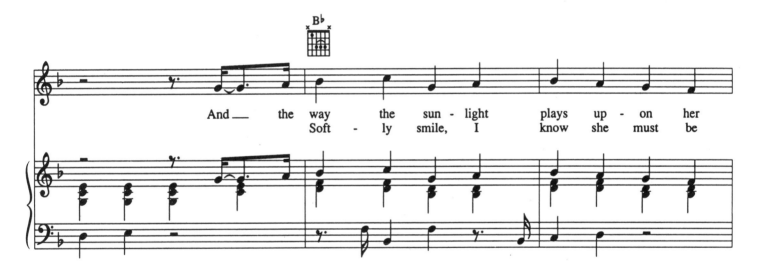

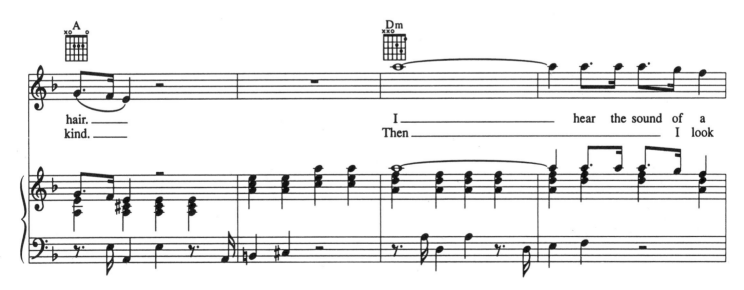

gen - tle word, _____ On _____ the wind that lifts her
in her eyes, _____ She _____ goes with me to a

per - fume through the air. _____
blos - som world. _____

Chorus

I'm pick - ing up good vi - bra - tions, She's giv - ing me

ex - ci - ta - tions. I'm pick - ing up good vi - bra - tions,

(Everything I Do) I Do It For You

Words by Bryan Adams & Robert John 'Mutt' Lange
Music by Michael Kamen

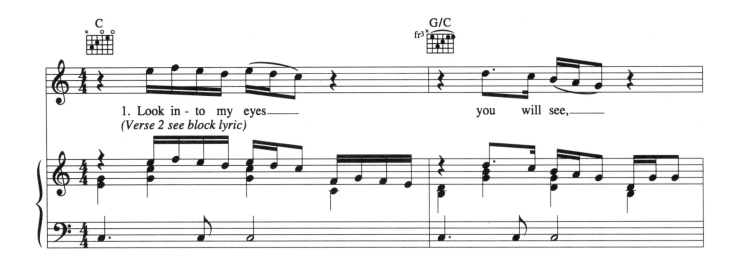

1. Look in - to my eyes_____ you will see,_____
(Verse 2 see block lyric)

what you mean to_____ me. Search your heart,_____ search your

soul,_____ and when you find me there you'll search_____ no more. Don't

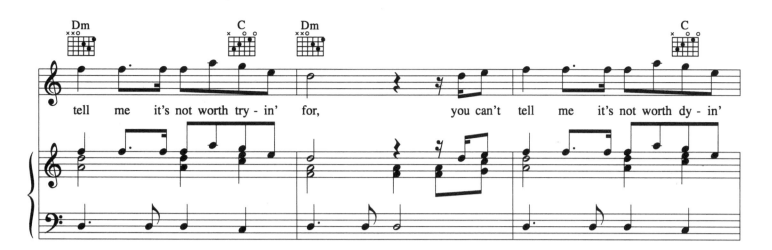

tell me it's not worth try-in' for, you can't tell me it's not worth dy-in'

for. You know it's true,_____ ev-ery-thing I do, I do it for—

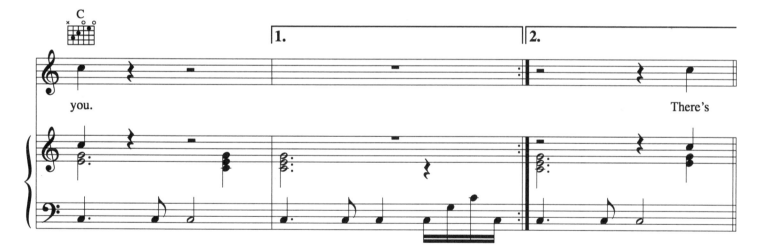

you. There's

no love like your love and no oth - er could give

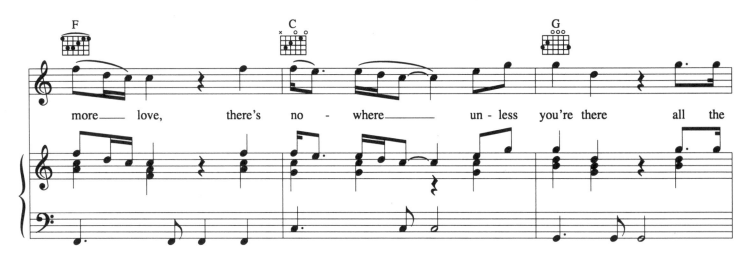

more—— love, there's no - where——— un - less you're there all the

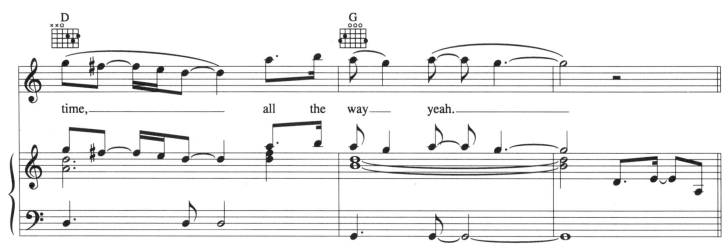

time,——————— all the way—— yeah.—————

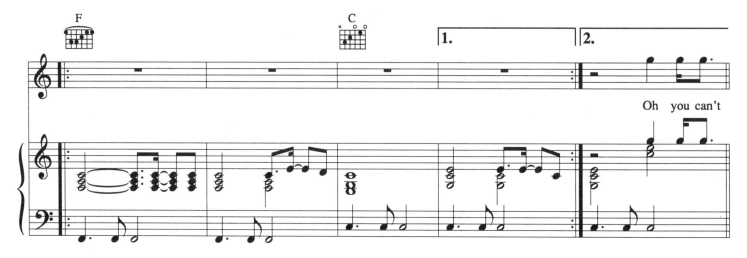

1.   2.

Oh you can't

tell me it's not worth fight-ing for,   I can't help—— it, there's no-thin' I want more.   Yeah— I would

fight for you,— I'd lie— for you,— walk the wire for you,— yeah— I'd

die for— you.— You know it's true, ev-ery-thing I

do, oh,———— I do it for— you.

Verse 2:
Look into your heart
You will find there's nothin' there to hide
Take me as I am, take my life
I would give it all, I would sacrifice.

Don't tell me it's not worth fightin' for
I can't help it, there's nothin' I want more
You know it's true, everything I do
I do it for you.

Hey Jude

Words & Music by John Lennon & Paul McCartney

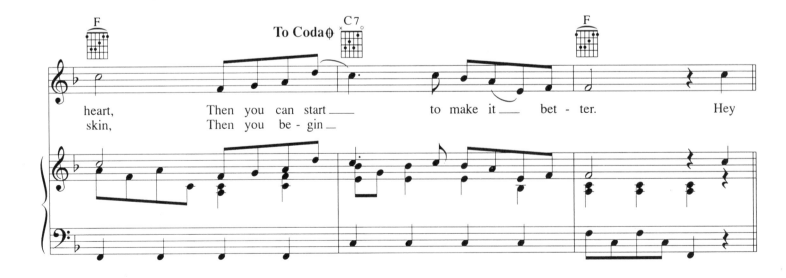

2. Jude, _____ don't be a-fraid. You were made to _____ go out and
3. Jude, _____ don't let me down. You have found her _____ now go and

get her. _____ The min-ute you let her un-der your
get her. _____ Re-mem-ber to let her in-to your

skin, Then you be-gin _____ to make it _____ bet-ter.
heart, Then you can start _____ to make it _____ bet-ter.

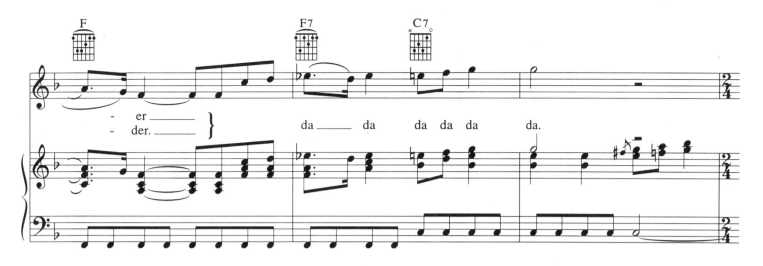

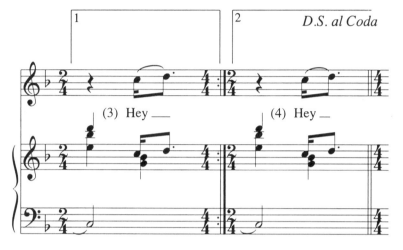

I Will Always Love You

Words & Music by Dolly Parton

Recite:
I hope that life treats you kind,
and I hope you have all that you ever dreamed of,
and I wish you joy and happiness,
but above all this, I wish you love.

Sing:
And I will always love you,
I will always love you,
I will always love you,
And I will always love you,
I will always love you,
I will always love you.

I Will Survive

Words & Music by Dino Fekaris & Freddie Perre

PolyGram Music Publishing Limited, 47 British Grove, London W4.

71

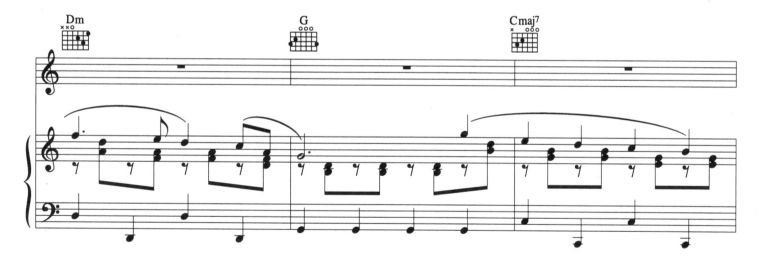

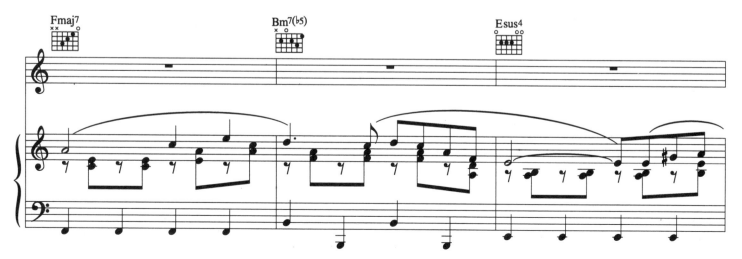

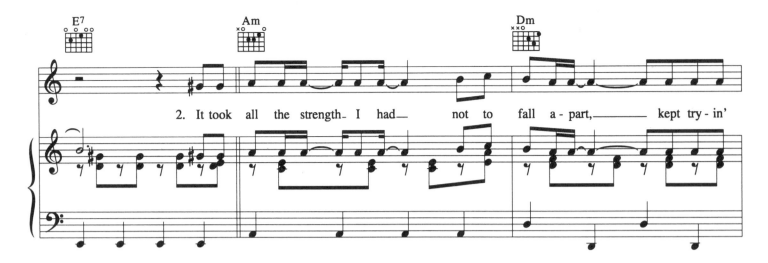

2. It took all the strength I had— not to fall a-part,———— kept try-in'

hard to mend— the pie-ces of my bro-ken heart,-—— and I spent oh so ma-ny nights— just feel-in'

D.%. al Coda

sor-ry for my-self.. I used to cry——— but now I hold my head up high— and you see

⊕ Coda

I'll sur-vive.——————

If You Leave Me Now

Words & Music by Peter Cetera

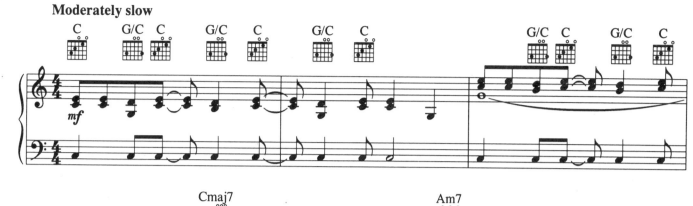

If you leave me now, ___ you'll take a -way the big - gest part ___
leave me now, ___ you'll take a -way the ver - y heart ___

___ of me. ___ Ooh, _____ no, ___ ba -by, please ___
___ of me. ___ Ooh, _____ no, ___ ba -by, please ___

___ don't go. _____ And if you
___ don't go. _ Ooh, _____

75

girl, _____ I just want you to stay. _____

A love ___ like ours ___ is love ___
We've come ___ too far ___ to leave ___

___ that's hard ___ to find. _____
___ it all ___ be-hind. _____

How could we let ___
How could we end ___

___ it _ slip _ a-way?
___ it _ all _ this way?

_____ When to-mor-

-row comes,__ then we'll both __ re-gret __ the things we said __ to - day.__

To Coda ⊕

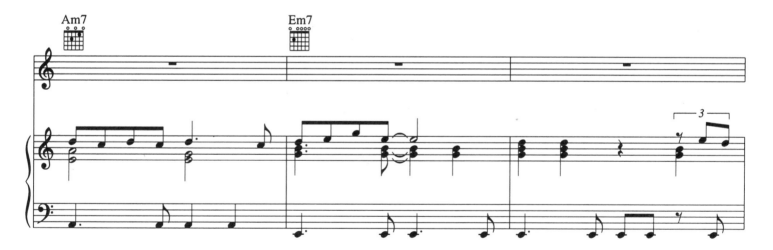

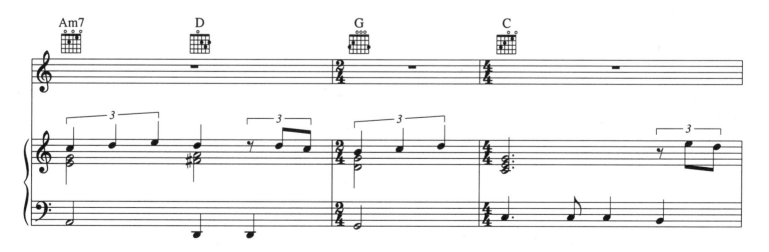

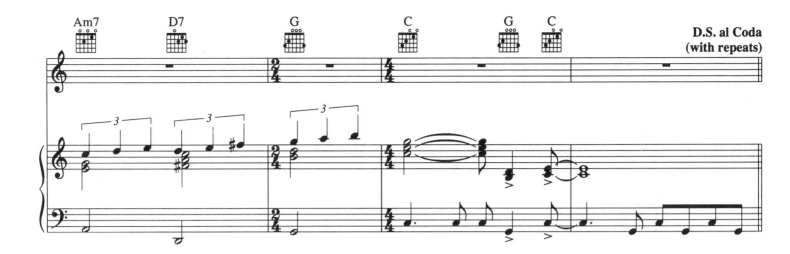

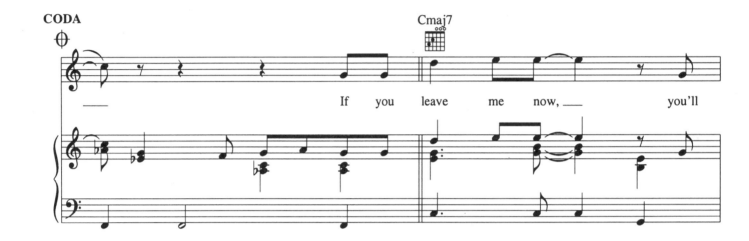

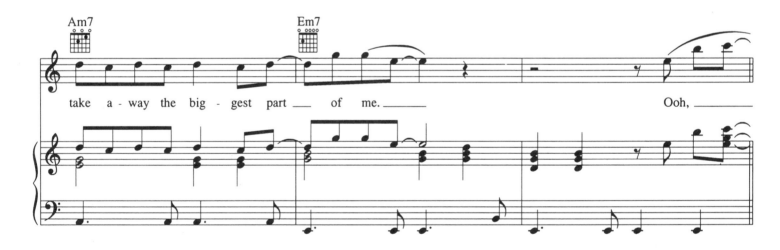

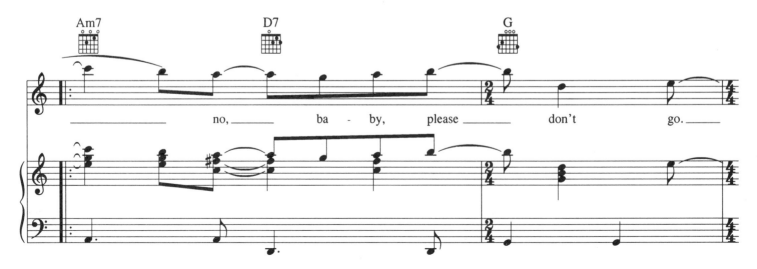

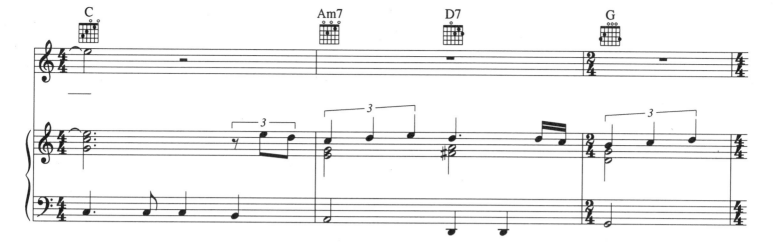

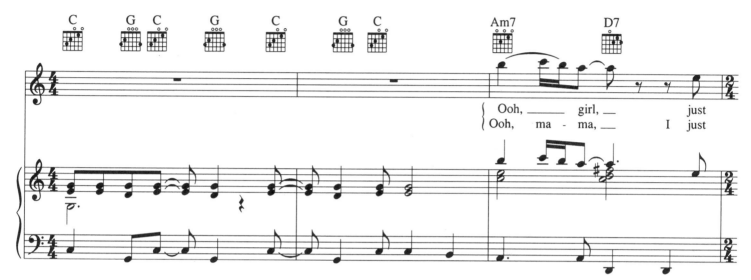

Ooh, _____ girl, _____ just
Ooh, ma - ma, _____ I just

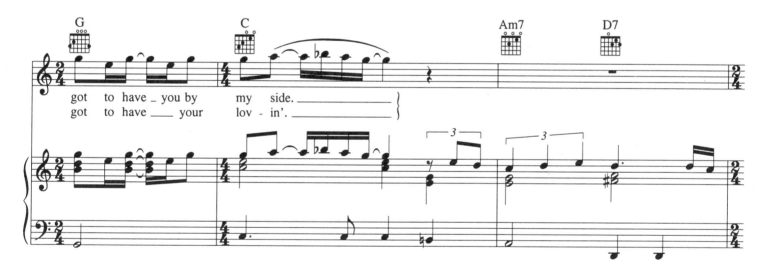

got to have _ you by _ my side. _____
got to have _____ your lov - in'. _____

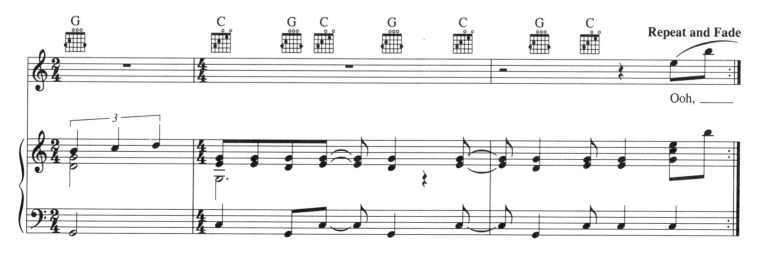

Repeat and Fade

Ooh, _____

(Just Like) Starting Over

Words & Music by John Lennon

let's take a chance and fly a-way___ some-where a - lone.___ It's

Moderately, with a strong beat

been too long since we took the time. No one's to blame. I know time flies___ so
day we used to make it, love.___ Why can't we be mak-in' love nice and

quick - ly!
ea - sy?
But
It's

when I see you, dar - lin', it's like we
time to spread our wings and fly. Don't let an -

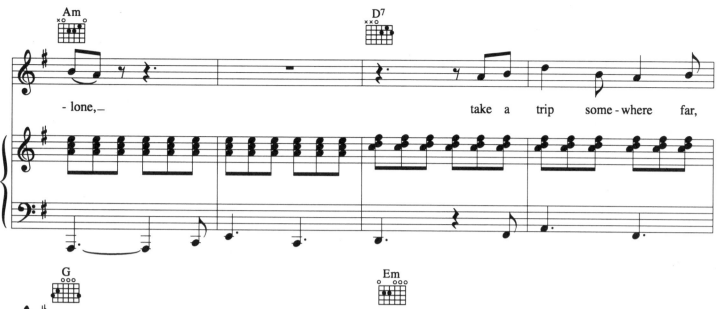

- lone,— take a trip some-where far,

far a - way.— We'll be to - geth - er all a-

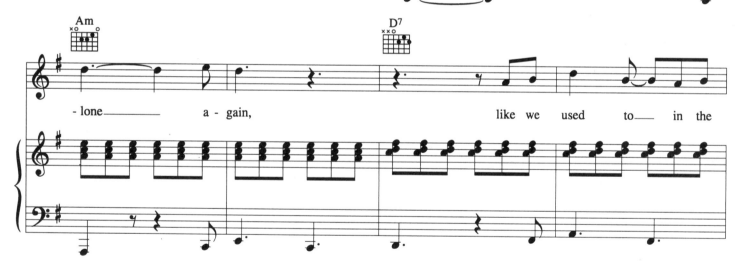

- lone———— a - gain, like we used to— in the

D.%. al Coda
(Repeat verse 1)

ear - ly days.— Well, well, dar - lin'. It's

Just The Two Of Us

Words & Music by Ralph MacDonald, William Salter & Bill Withers

first time the doc-tor placed you in my arms I knew— I'd meet death be-fore I'd let you meet harm. Al-though
(Verses 2 & 3 see block lyric)

ques-tions a - rose— in my mind, would I be man e - nough?— Against wrong choose right and be stand-in' up.

From the hos - pi - tal that first night took a hour just to get the car - seat in right.— Peo-ple

driv-in' all fast, got me kin-da up-set.— Got you home safe, placed you in your ba-son-ette. That

Coda

two of us, _____ you and I. _____ Tru-dat, _____ tru-dat. (Just the two of us.)

(Just the two of us.) (Just the two of us.)(That's a really good song. How much am I getting paid for this Dad?)

Verse 2:

Five years old, bringin' comedy
Everytime I look at you I think man, a little me
Just like me, wait and see gonna be tall
Makes me laugh cause you got your dad's ears and all
Sometimes I wonder, what you gonna be
A General, a Doctor, maybe a MC?
Haha, I wanna kiss you all the time
But I will test that butt when you cut outta line, trudat
Uh-uh-uh why do you do that?
I try to be a tough dad, but you be makin' me laugh
Crazy joy, when I see the eyes of my baby boy
I pledge to you, I will always do everything I can
Show you how to be a man
Dignity, integrity, honour and
I don't mind if you lose, long as you came with it
And you can cry, aint no shame in it
It didn't work out with me and your Mom
But yo, push come to shove, you was conceived in love
So if the world attacks, and you slide off track
Remember one fact, I got your back.

Just the two of us *etc.*

Verse 3:

It's a full-time job to be a good dad
You got so much more stuff than I had
I gotta study just to keep with the changin' times
101 Dalmations on your CD-ROM
See me, I'm tryin' to pretend I know
On my PC where dat CD go
But yo, ain't nuthin' promised, one day I'll be gone
Feel the strife, but trust life does go on
But just in case, it's my place to impart
One day some girl's gonna break your heart
And ooh ain't no pain like from the oppsite sex
Gonna hurt bad, but don't take it out on the next, son
Throughout life people will make you mad
Disrespect you and treat you bad
Let God deal with the things they do
Cause hate in your heart will consume you too
Always tell the truth, say your prayers
Hold doors, pull out chairs, easy on the swears
You're living proof that dreams come true
I love you and I'm here for you.

Just the two of us *etc.*

Imagine

Words & Music by John Lennon

tries.
ions.

It is-n't hard____ to do.
I won-der if you____ can.

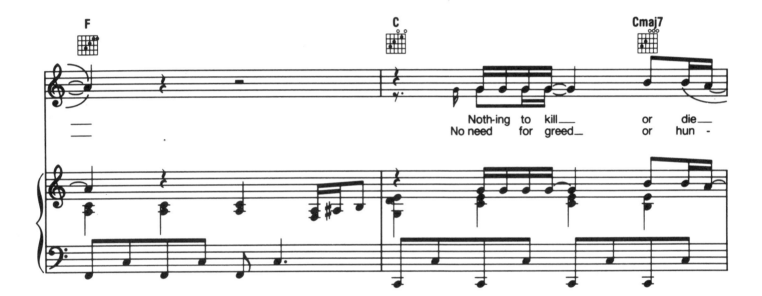

Noth-ing to kill____ or die____
No need for greed____ or hun -

____ for
ger,

and no re-li-gion,____ too.____
a broth-er-hood____ of man.____

Layla

Words & Music by Eric Clapton & Jim Gordon

Moderately, with a beat

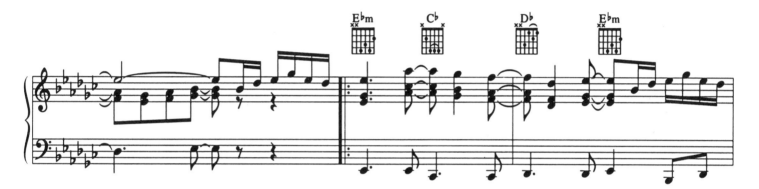

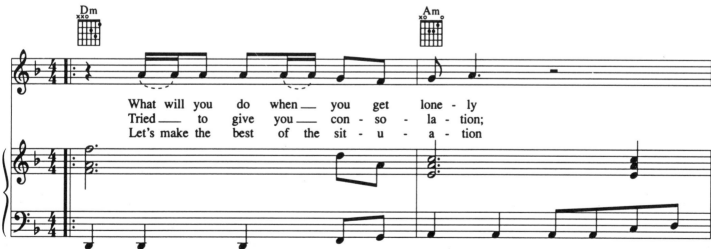

What will you do when ___ you get lone - ly
Tried ___ to give you ___ con - so - la - tion;
Let's make the best of the sit - u - a - tion

with no-bo-dy wait-ing by your ___ side?
your ___ old man won't let you ___ down.
be-fore ___ I fi-n'lly go in - sane.

You've been run-ning and
Like a fool, ___ I
Please don't say ___ we'll

hid-ing much too long; ___
fell in love with you; ___
nev-er find a way ___

You know, it's just your fool-ish pride.
turned the whole world up - side down.
and tell me all my love's ___ in vain.

} Lay - -

la, ___ you got me on ___ my knees. Lay - la, ___ I'm

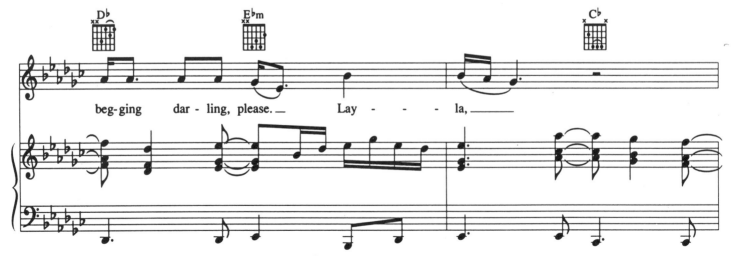

beg-ging dar - ling, please. ___ Lay - - la, ___

dar-ling, won't you ease my wor-ried mind?

mind?   Lay - la, ___   you got me on ___ my knees. Lay -

la, ___   I'm beg-ging dar-ling, please. ___ Lay - la, ___

dar-ling, won't you ease my wor-ried mind?

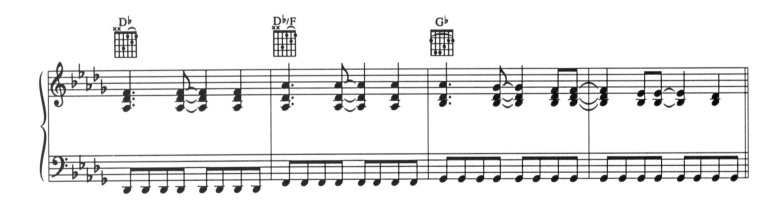

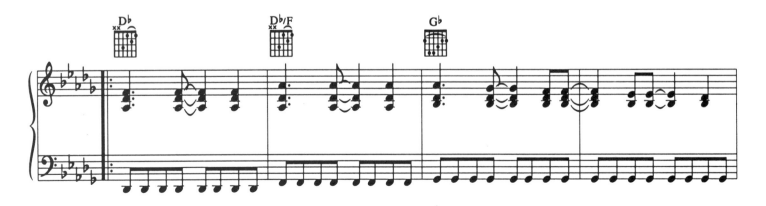

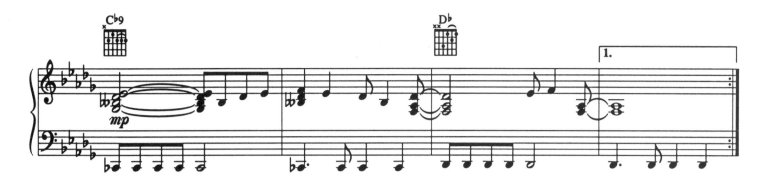

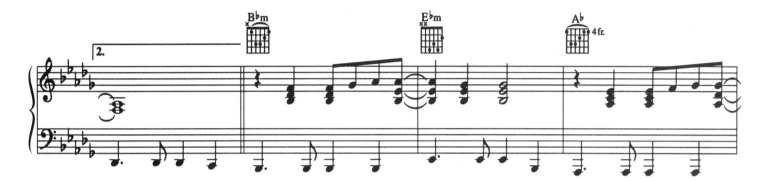

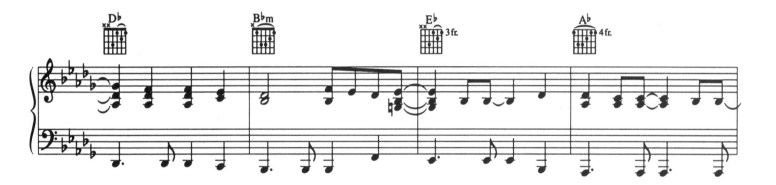

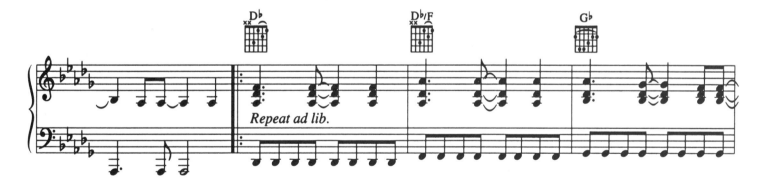

Repeat ad lib.

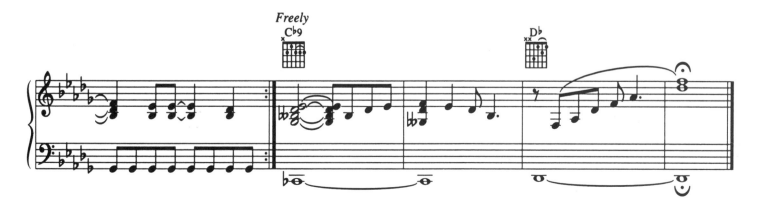

Freely

Let It Be

Words & Music by John Lennon & Paul McCartney

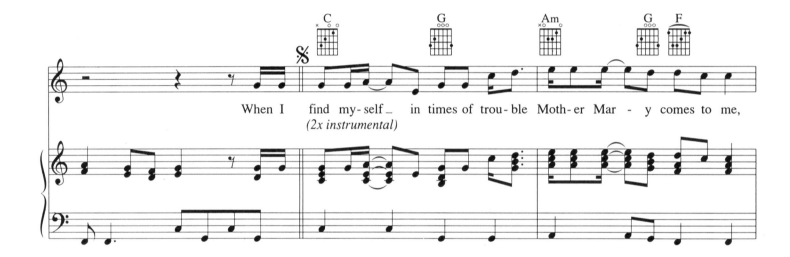

When I find my-self _ in times of trou-ble Moth-er Mar - y comes to me,
(2x instrumental)

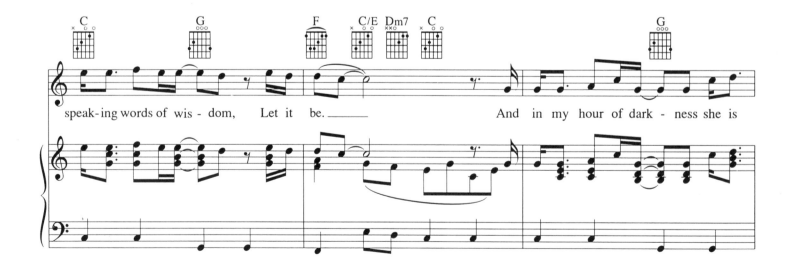

speak-ing words of wis - dom, Let it be. _____ And in my hour of dark - ness she is

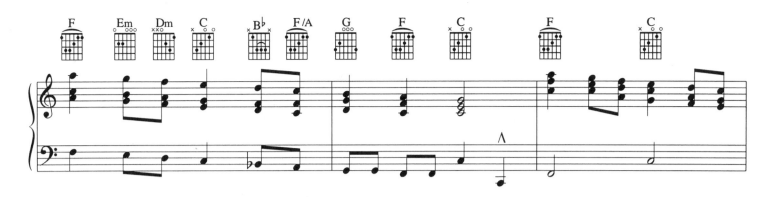

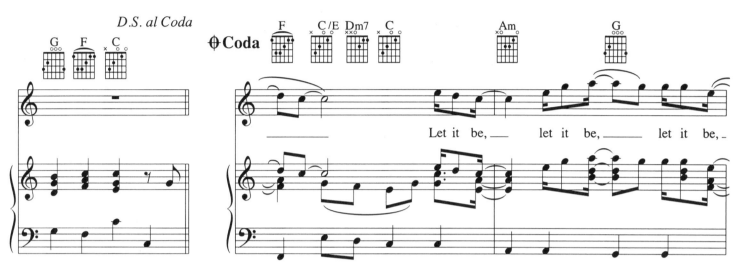

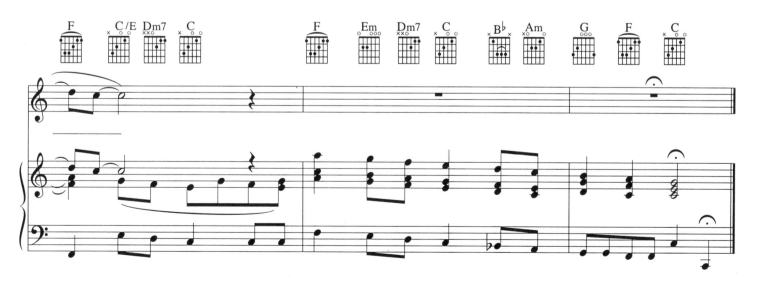

Like A Rolling Stone

Words & Music by Bob Dylan

kid - din' you   You used to

laugh a - bout   Ev-'ry-bod-y that was

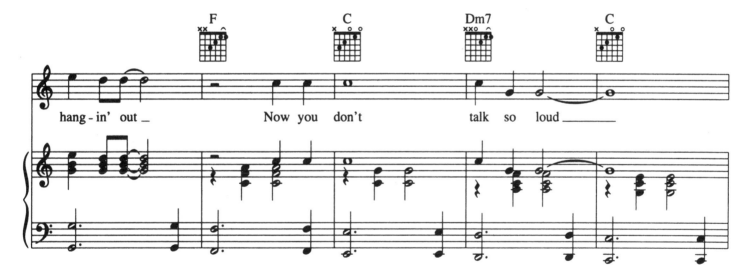

hang - in' out __   Now you don't   talk so loud _____

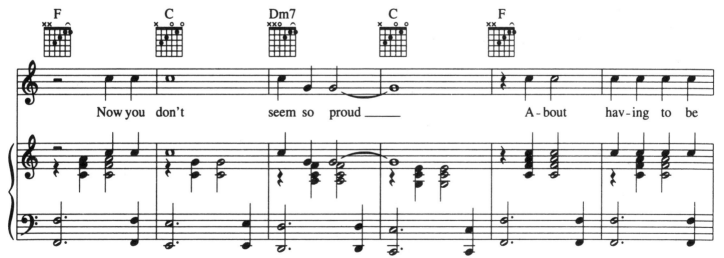

Now you don't   seem so proud _____   A - bout   hav - ing to be   You used to

scroung - ing   for your next   meal. _____

chorus

How does it feel   How does it   feel

To be with-out a   home

Like a com-plete un-known   like a roll-ing   stone?

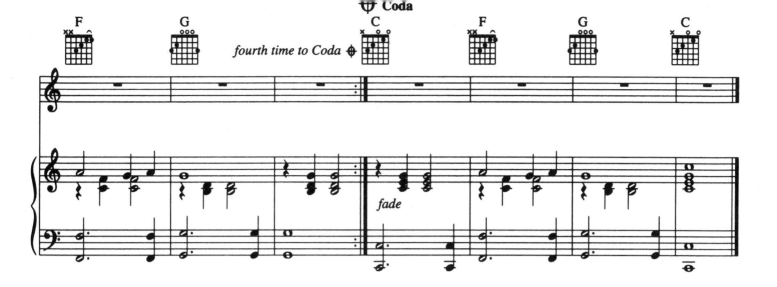

Additional lyrics

2. You've gone to the finest school all right Miss Lonely
   But you know you only used to get juiced in it
   And nobody's every taught you how to live on the street
   And now find out you're gonna have to get used to it
   You said you'd never compromise
   With the mystery tramp, but now you realize
   He's not selling any alibis
   As you stare into the vacuum of his eyes
   And ask him do you want to make a deal?
   Chorus

3. You never turned around to see the frowns on the jugglers and the clowns
   When they all come down and did tricks for you
   You never understood that it ain't no good
   You shouldn't let other people get your kicks for you
   You used to ride on the chrome horse with your diplomat
   Who carried on his shoulder a Siamese cat
   Ain't it hard when you discovered that
   He really wasn't where it's at
   After he took from you everything he could steal.
   Chorus

4. Princess on the steeple and all the pretty people
   They're drinkin', thinkin' that they got it made
   Exchanging all kinds of precious gifts and things
   But you'd better lift your diamond ring, you'd better pawn it babe
   You used to be so amused
   At Napoleon in rags and the language that he used
   Go to him now, he calls you, you can't refuse
   When you got nothing, you got nothing to lose
   You're invisible now, you got no secrets to conceal.
   Chorus

Love Me Do

Words & Music by John Lennon & Paul McCartney

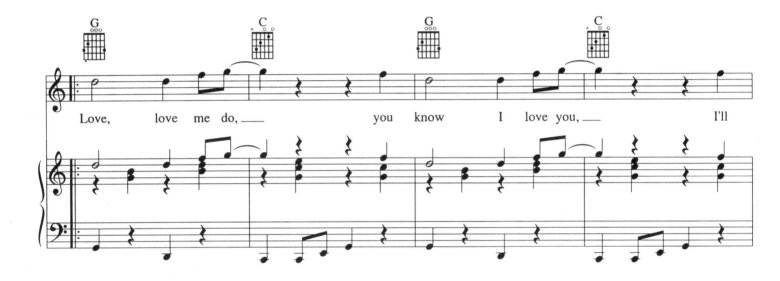

Love, love me do, ____ you know I love you, ____ I'll

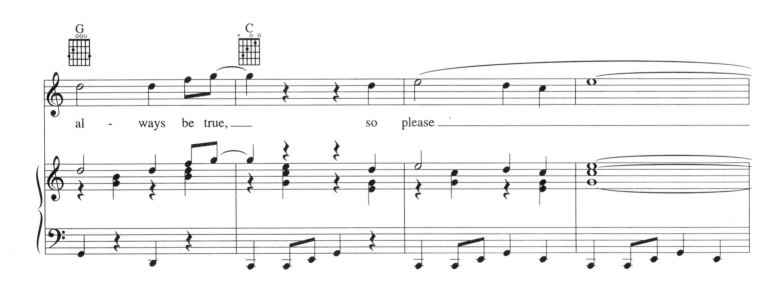

al - ways be true, ____ so please _____ I'll

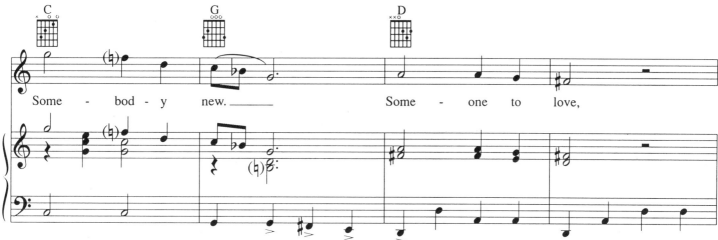

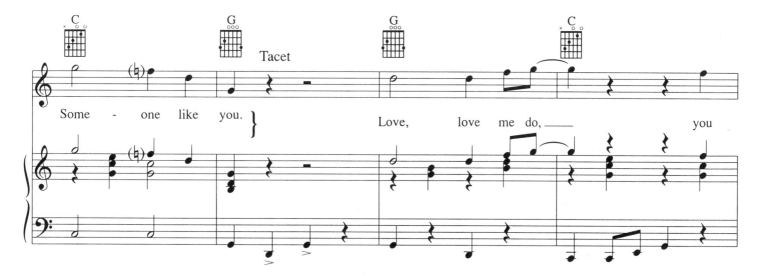

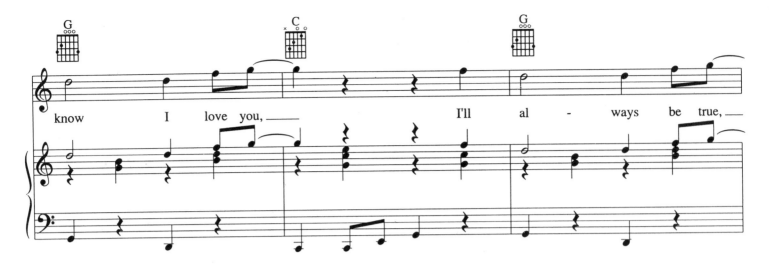

know I love you, _____ I'll al - ways be true, _____

so please _____ Love me

Tacet

do. _____ Woh, _____ love ____ me do. ____

Woh, _____ love ____ me do. ____

Repeat and Fade

Millennium

Music by Guy Chambers, Robbie Williams & John Barry
Words by Guy Chambers, Robbie Williams & Leslie Bricusse

Mil - len - ni - um.___ Some say that we are play - ers, some say that we are pawns,___ but

we've been mak - ing mo - ney since___ the day___ that we were born, got to slow

down,___ 'cos we're low___ down.___

Run a - round in cir - cles, live a life___ of so - li - tude,___ till we find

Live for li - po - suc - tion and de - tox for your rent,___

'cos we know____ we're fall - ing from grace.____

Mil - len - ni - um.____

Come and have____ a go____ if you____ think you____ are high____ e - nough.

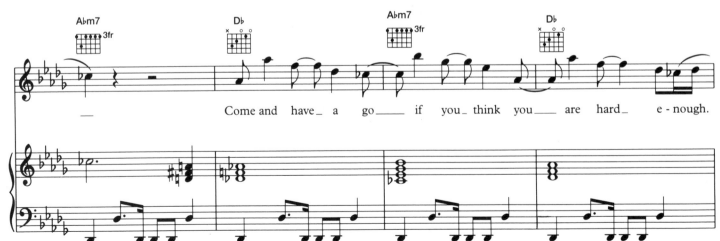

Come and have____ a go____ if you___ think you____ are hard____ e - nough.

Mil - len - ni - um. _____ Mil - len - ni - um. ____

We've got stars ____ di - rect - ing our fate ____

and we're pray - ing it's ____ not too late, ____

'cos we know ____ we're fall - ing from grace. ____

Mull Of Kintyre

Words & Music by McCartney & Laine

moun-tains___ with val-leys___ of green. Past paint-ed des-erts___ the

sun-set's on fire___ as he car - ries me home___ to the Mull___ of Kin-

tyre. Mull___ of Kin - tyre Oh mist roll -ing in from___ the

sea, my de - sire is al - ways to be here Oh Mull___ of Kin-

tyre.

Sweep through the heath-er___ like deer in the

glen   Car-ry me back to the days I knew then.   Nights when we

Mr. Tambourine Man

Words & Music by Bob Dylan

fifth time Fine

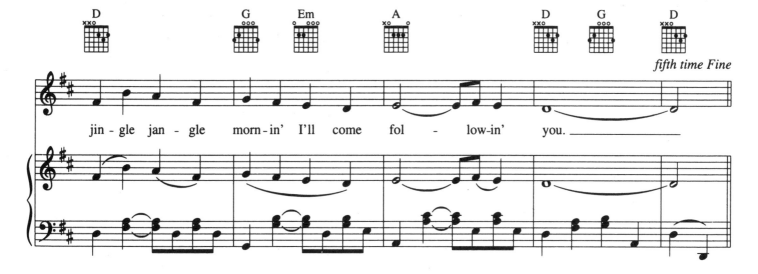

jin - gle jan - gle morn - in' I'll come fol - low - in' you.

Verse

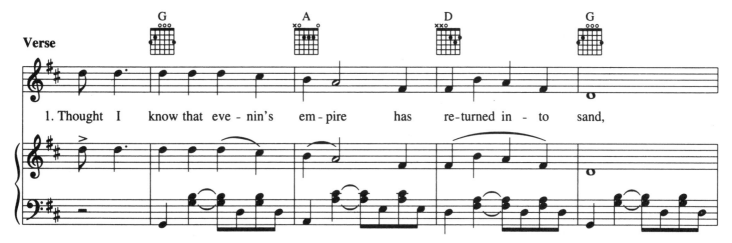

1. Thought I know that eve - nin's em - pire has re - turned in - to sand,

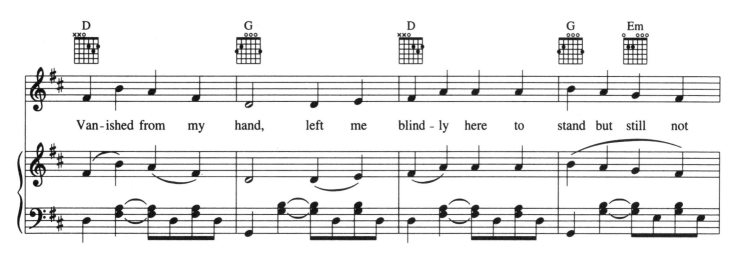

Van - ished from my hand, left me blind - ly here to stand but still not

sleep - in'! My wea - ri - ness a - maz - es me I'm

125

Refrain:

Verse 2. Take me on a trip upon your magic swirlin' ship
My senses have been stripped, my hands can't feel to grip
My toes too numb to step, wait only for my boot heels
To be wanderin'
I'm ready to go anywhere, I'm ready for to fade
Into my own parade, cast your dancin' spell my way
I promise to go under it.

Refrain:

Verse 3. Though you might hear laughin' spinnin' swingin' madly across the sun
It's not aimed at anyone, it's just escapin' on the run
And but for the sky there are no fences facin'
And if you hear vague traces of skippin' reels of rhyme
To your tambourine in time, it's just a ragged clown behind
I wouldn't pay it any mind, it's just a shadow you're
Seein' that he's chasin'.

Refrain:

Verse 4. Then take me disappearin' through the smoke rings of my mind
Down the foggy ruins of time, far past the frozen leaves
The haunted, frightened trees out to the windy beach
Far from the twisted reach of crazy sorrow
Yes, to dance beneath the diamond sky with one hand wavin' free
Silhouetted by the sea, circled by the circus sands
With all memory and fate driven deep beneath the waves
Let me forget about today until tomorrow.

Refrain:

What Can I Do

Words & Music by Andrea Corr, Caroline Corr, Sharon Corr & Jim Corr

1. I have-n't slept at all in days;
(Verse 3 see block lyric)

It's been so long since we have talked.

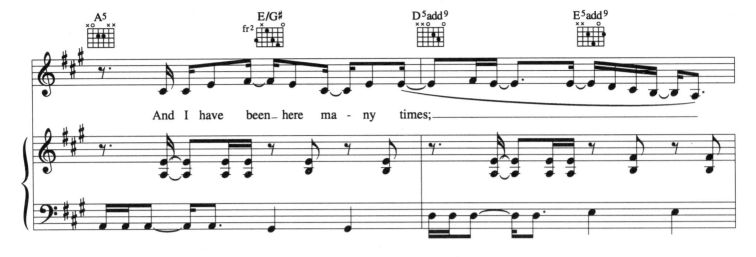

And I have been here ma - ny times;

To Coda ⊕

I just don't know what I'm do - in' wrong.

What can I do to make you love me?

What can I do to make you care?

What can I say— to make— you feel— this?

What can I do— to get— you there?—

2. There's on-ly so— much I— can take,—

And I just got-ta let— it go.—

To love,— love me?_____ Love me,— love_____

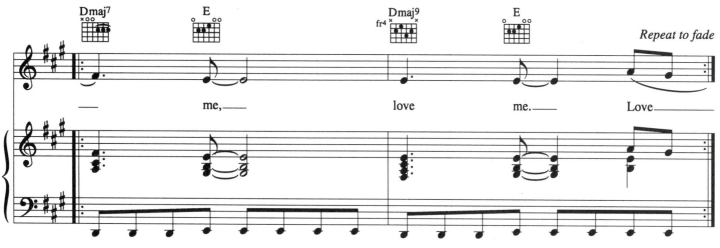

Repeat to fade

— me,_____ love me._____ Love_____

Verse 3:
Maybe there's nothing more to say;
And, in a funny way, I'm calm.
Because the power is not mine,
I'm just gonna let it fly.

No Woman, No Cry

Words & Music by Bob Marley & Vincent Ford

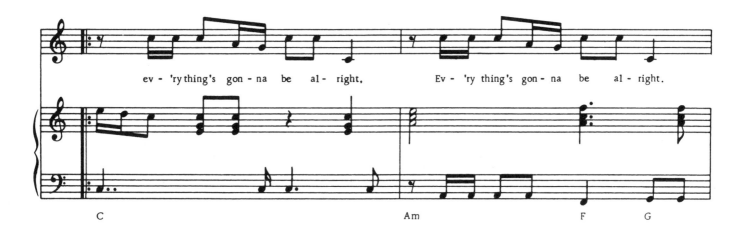

ev - 'ry thing's gon - na be al - right,   Ev - 'ry thing's gon - na be al - right.

C   Am   F   G

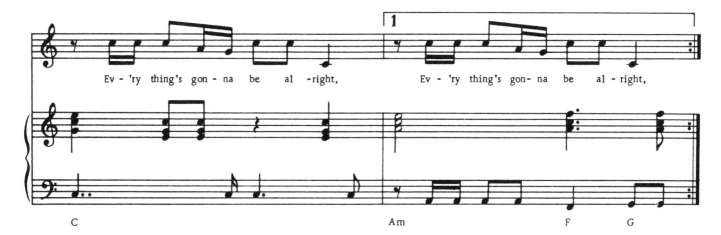

Ev - 'ry thing's gon - na be al - right,   Ev - 'ry thing's gon - na be al - right,

C   Am   F   G

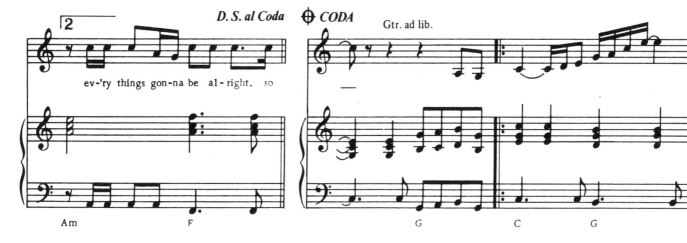

D. S. al Coda   ✛ *CODA*   Gtr. ad lib.

ev - 'ry things gon - na be al - right, so

Am   F   G   C   G

To fade

Am   F   C   F   C   G

Night Fever

Words & Music by Barry Gibb, Robin Gibb & Maurice Gibb

Lis - ten to__ the ground:__ there is move-ment all__ a - round.__ There is
heat of our__ love,__ don't need no help for us__ to make__ it. Gim - me

some-thing go - in' down,__ and I can feel it. On the
just e - nough__ to take__ us to the morn - in'. I got

waves of __ the air, __ there is danc-in' out __ there. __ If it's
fire in __ my mind. __ I got high-er in __ my walk-in'. And I'm

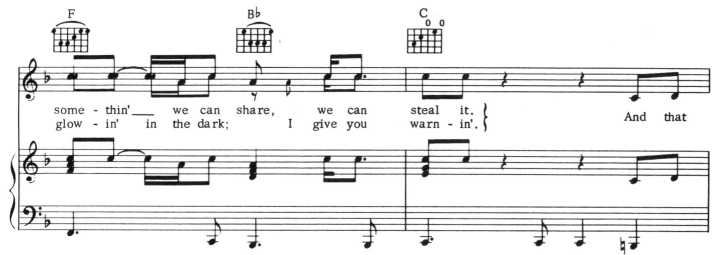

some-thin' __ we can share, we can steal it.
glow-in' in the dark; I give you warn-in'.
And that

sweet cit-y wom-an, she moves through the light, __ con-

trol-ling my mind __ and my soul. __ When you

reach out for me,___ yeah, and the feel-in' is___ bright, then I get

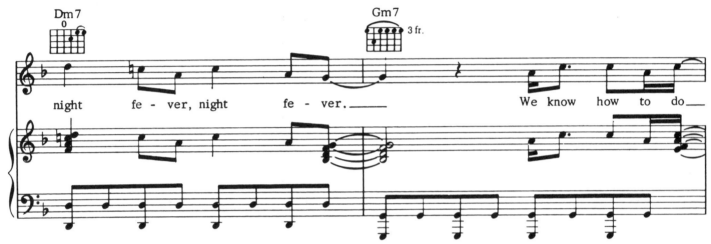

night fe-ver, night fe-ver.___ We know how to do___

___ it. Gim-me that

night fe-ver, night fe-ver.___ We know how to show___

Here I am, pray-in' for this mo-ment to last,_____ liv-in' on the mu-sic so fine,_____ borne on the wind,_ mak-in' it mine._____

Penny Lane

Words & Music by John Lennon & Paul McCartney

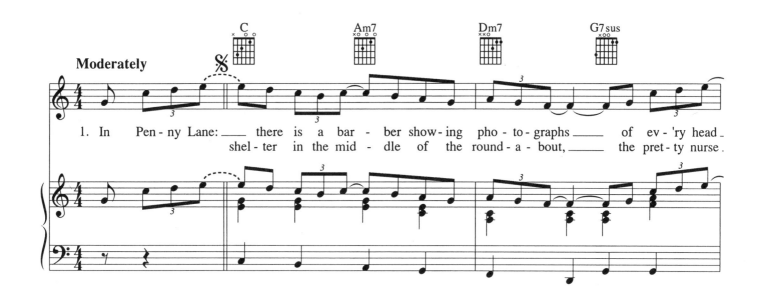

Moderately

1. In Pen - ny Lane: ____ there is a bar - ber show - ing pho - to - graphs ____ of ev - 'ry head ___
shel - ter in the mid - dle of the round - a - bout, ____ the pret - ty nurse _

_ he's had the pleas - ure to know, ____ And all the peo - ple that come and go ___
_ is sell - ing pop - pies from a tray. ___ And tho' she feels as if she's in a play _

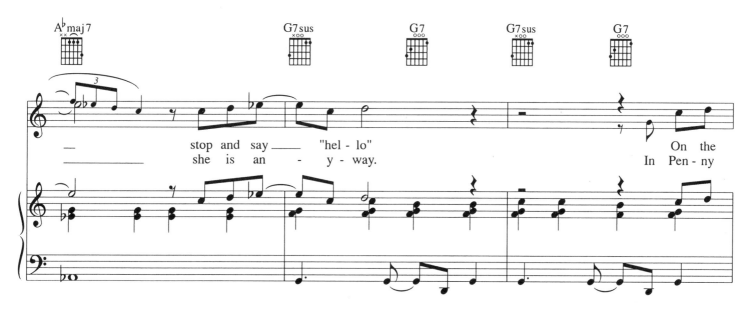

__ stop and say ___ "hel - lo" _____ On the
she is an - y - way. _____ In Pen - ny

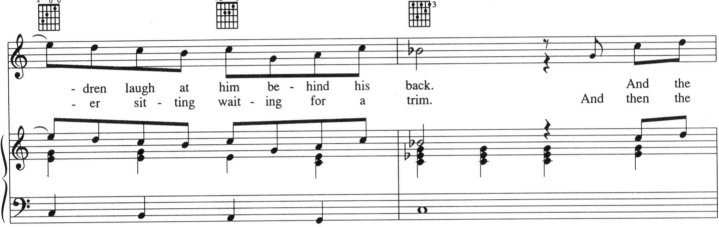
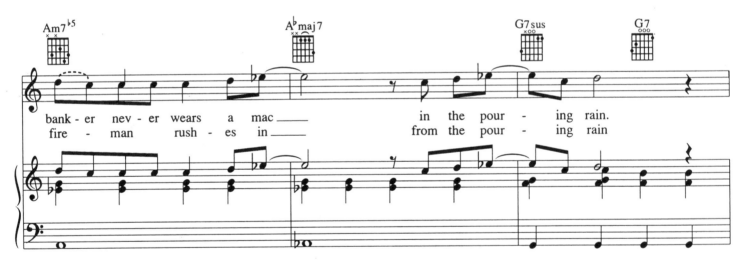

There be - neath the blue ___ sub - ur - ban skies ___
There be - neath the blue ___ sub - ur - ban skies ___

To Coda ⊕

___ I sit. And mean - while back in Pen - ny Lane ___ there is a fire - man with an
___ I sit. And

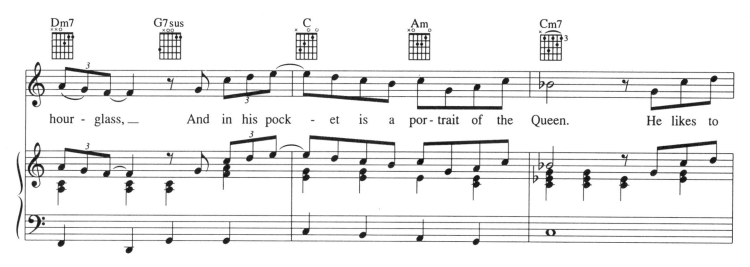

hour - glass, ___ And in his pock - et is a por - trait of the Queen. He likes to

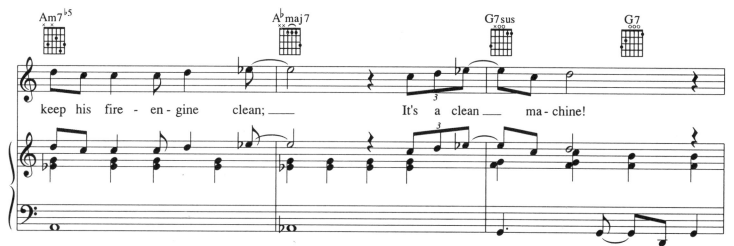

keep his fire - en - gine clean; ___ It's a clean ___ ma - chine!

Pen - ny Lane ____ is in my ears ____

____ and in my eyes. ____ Full of fish ____

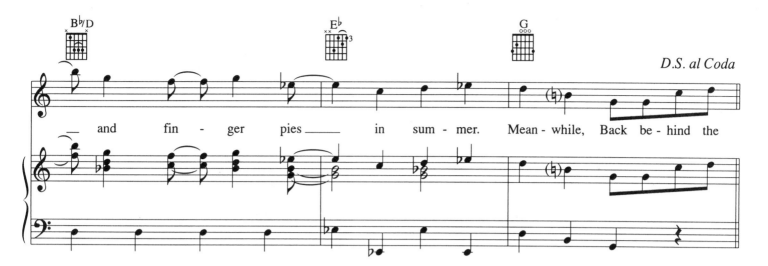

D.S. al Coda

and fin - ger pies _____ in sum - mer. Mean - while, Back be - hind the

Coda

mean - while back, Pen - ny Lane _____ is in my ears _____ and in my eyes. _____

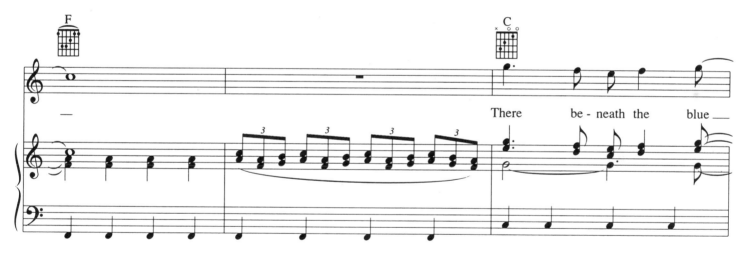

_____ There be - neath the blue _____

_____ sub - ur - ban skies _____ Pen - ny Lane _____

One Moment In Time

Words & Music by Albert Hammond & John Bettis

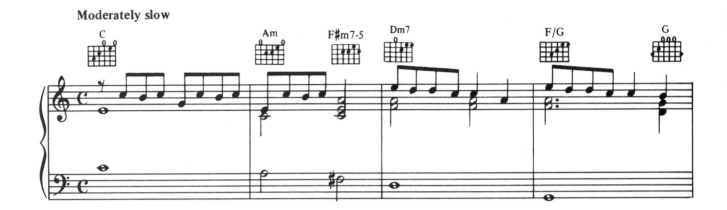

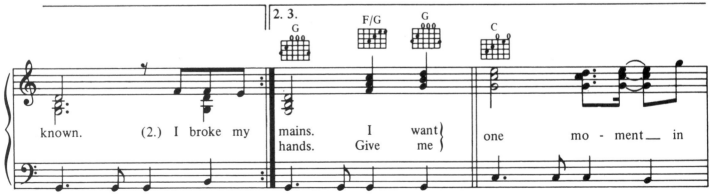

149

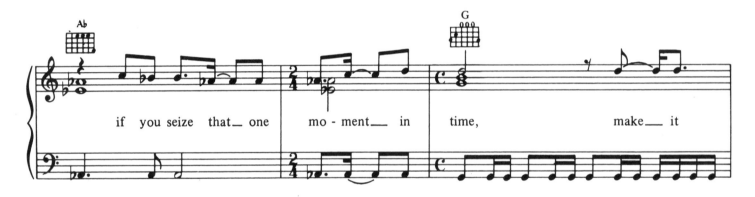

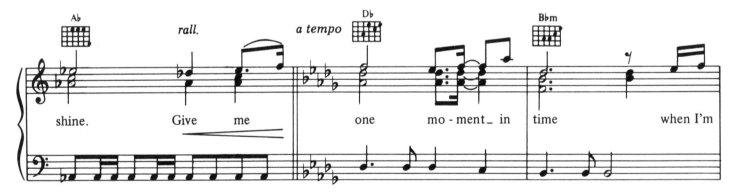

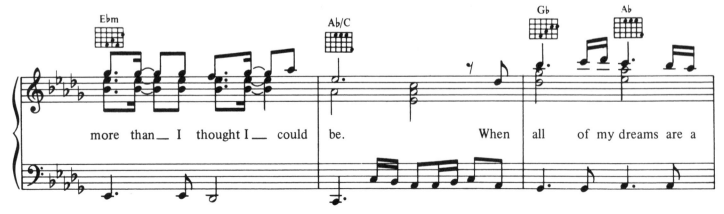

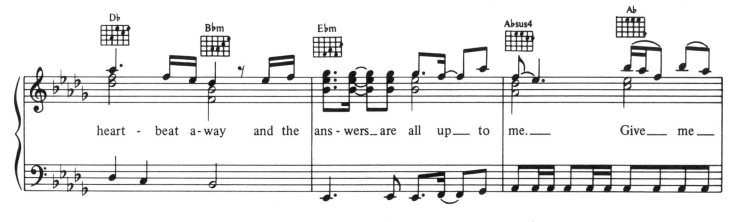

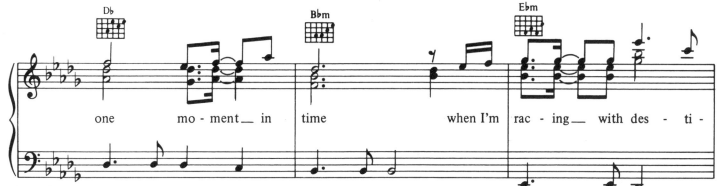

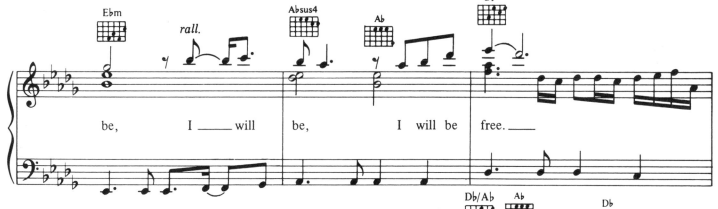

Sweet Dreams Are Made Of This

Words & Music by D. A. Stewart & A. Lennox

some of them want to get used _ by you, _ some of them want to ab-use _ you,

some of them want to be _ ab - used. _

Hold your head up, keep your head up, mov-in' on. __ Hold your head up, mov-in' on. __

Keep your head up, mov-in' on. __ Hold your head up, mov-in' on. __ Keep your head up, mov-in' on. __

(x 4)

D.S. & Repeat

Hold your head up, mov-in' on, __ keep your head up.

Take My Breath Away

Words by Tom Whitlock
Music by Giorgio Moroder

Moderately slow

mf

A♭   Cm/G

Fm   Cm/G   A♭

Watch-ing ev-'ry mo - tion in ___
Watch-ing, I keep wait - ing, still ___
Watch-ing ev-'ry mo - tion in ___

Cm/G   Fm

___ my fool - ish lov - er's game; ___
___ an - tic - i - pat - ing love, ___
___ this fool - ish lov - er's game; ___

Cm/G   A♭

on this end - less o - cean, fi -
nev - er hes - i - tat - ing to ___
haunt - ed by the no - tion some -

155

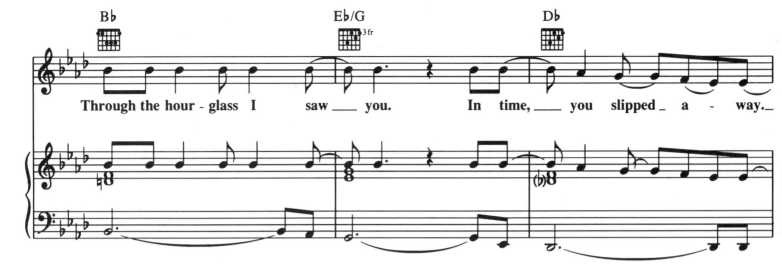

Through the hour - glass I saw ___ you. In time, ___ you slipped ___ a - way. ___

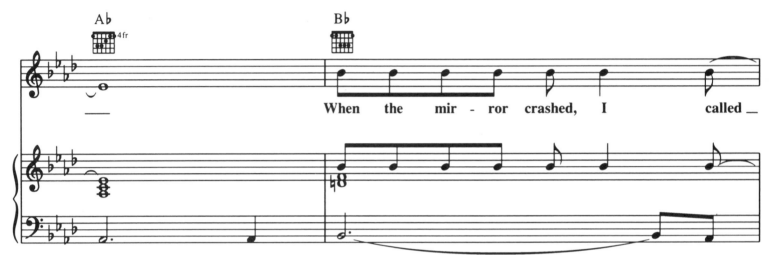

___ When the mir - ror crashed, I ___ called ___

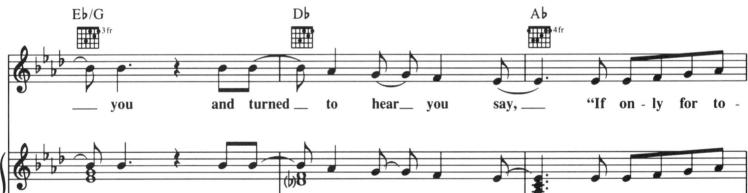

___ you and turned ___ to hear ___ you say, ___ "If on - ly for to -

day _____ I ___ am un - a - fraid. _____

Tears In Heaven

Words & Music by Eric Clapton & Will Jennings

Be - yond the door ___ there's peace, I'm sure.

And I know___ there'll be no more___ tears in heav-

en.

D.S. al Coda

CODA

en.

rall.

The Best

Words & Music by Mike Chapman & Holly Knight

(1.) I call you, I need you, my heart's on fire. _____
(Verses 2 & 3 see block lyric)

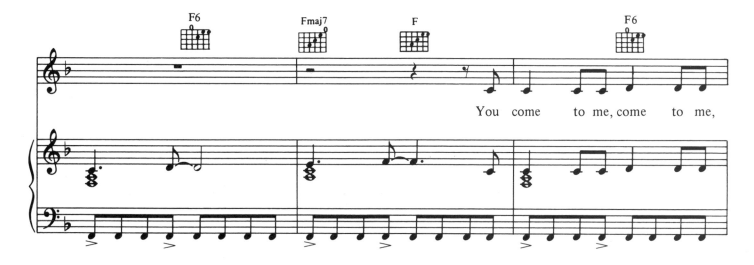

You come to me, come to me,

e - ver met.__ I'm stuck on your heart,__

I hang on ev-'ry word__ you say, __ tear us a-part__

To Coda ⊕ *D.% al Coda*

__ ba-by I would ra-ther be__ dead. (3.) In your

⊕ *CODA*

Each time you leave me, I start los-ing con-trol__ you're

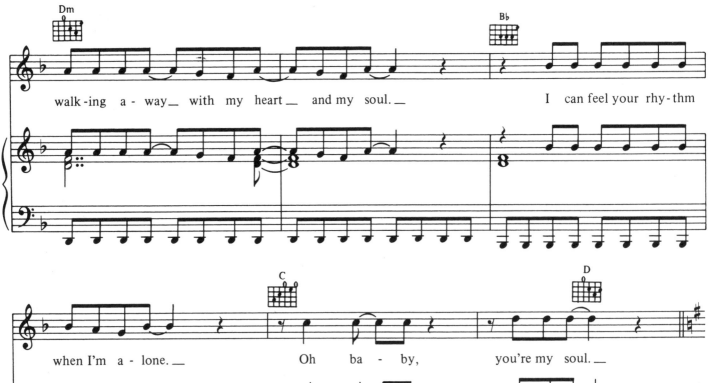

walk-ing a-way— with my heart— and my soul.—   I can feel your rhy-thm

when I'm a-lone. — Oh ba - by, you're my soul. —

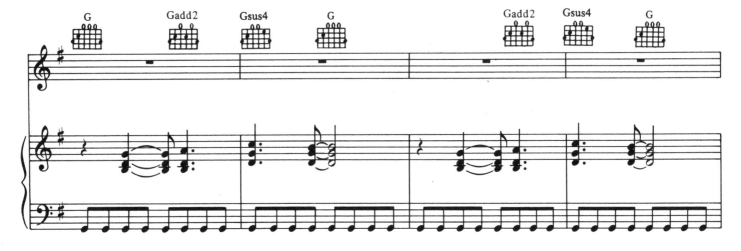

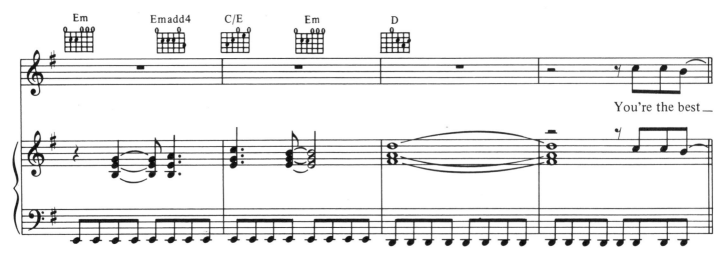

You're the best —

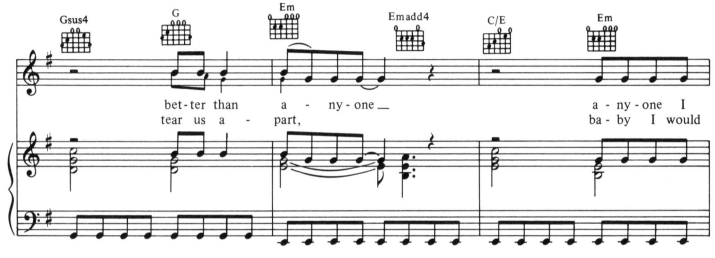

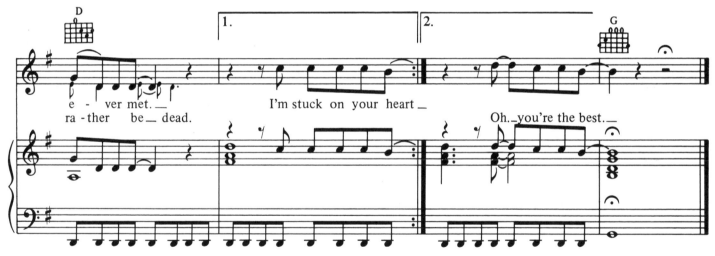

VERSE 2:
Give me a lifetime of promises, and a world of dreams
Speak the language of love like you know what it means
Mm, and it can't be wrong
Take my heart and make it strong babe.

VERSE 3:
In your heart, in the stars, every night and every day
In your eyes I get lost, I get washed away
Just as long as I'm here in your arms
I could be in no better place.

The Power Of Love

Words & Music by C. deRouge, G. Mende, J. Rush & S. Applegate

as I look— in your eyes.

I hold on— to your bo-dy,—

and feel each move you make,

your voice is warm and ten-der, a love that

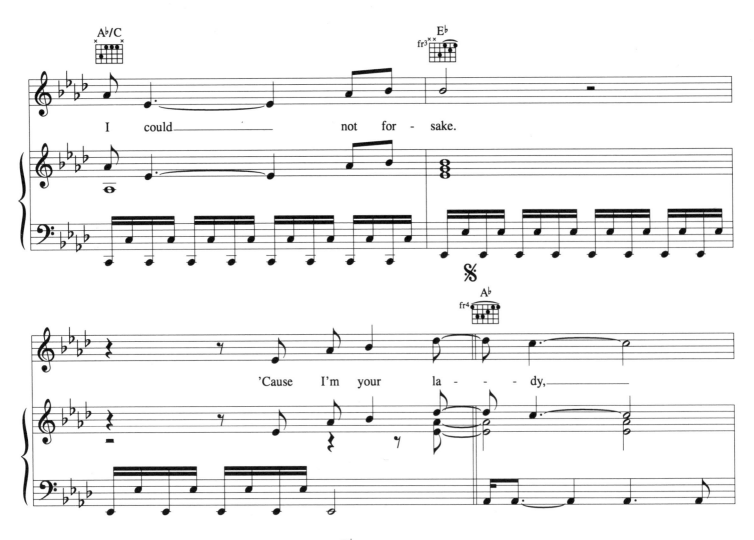

I could_____ not for - sake.

'Cause I'm your la - - dy,_____

and you are my man,_____ when - ev - er you reach

_____ for me, I'll do all that I can._____

2. Lost is how I'm We're head-ing for

some - thing, some - where I've ne - ver been,

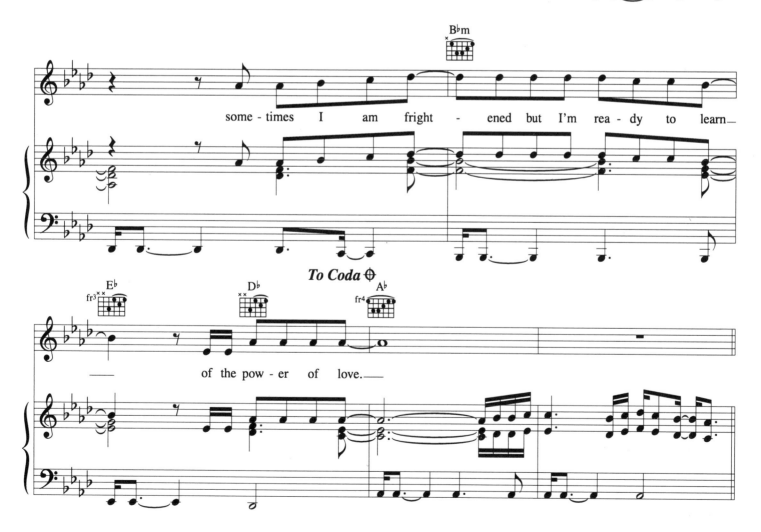

some - times I am fright - ened but I'm rea - dy to learn

To Coda ✛

of the pow - er of love.

The sound of your heart beat - ing made it clear sud-den-

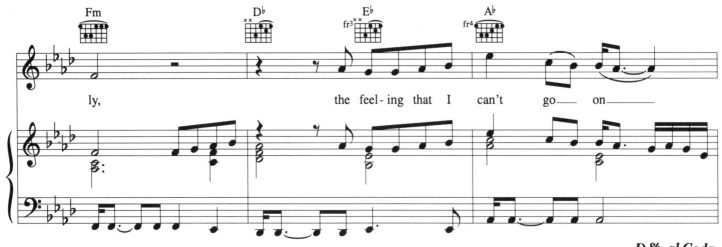

ly, the feel-ing that I can't go on

D.%. al Coda

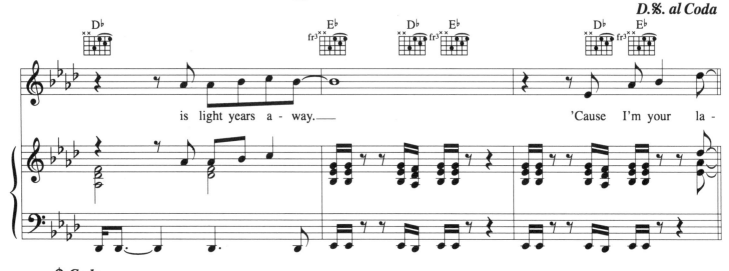

is light years a - way. 'Cause I'm your la-

⊕ *Coda*

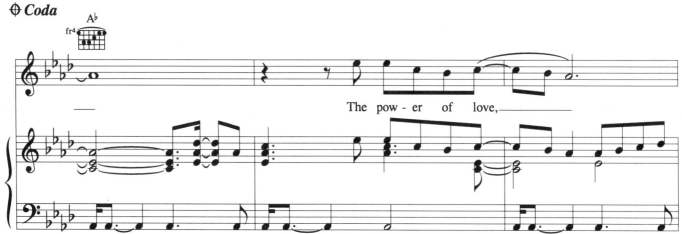

The pow-er of love,

the pow-er of love,_____ some-times I am fright-

-ened but I'm rea-dy to learn___ the pow-er of love.___

Repeat to fade

_____ The pow-er of love._

Verse 2:
Lost is how I'm feeling
Lying in your arms,
When the world outside's too much to take,
That all ends when I'm with you.
Even though there may be times
It seems I'm far away,
Never wonder where I am
'Cause I am always by your side.

175

Torn

Words & Music by Anne Preven, Scott Cutler & Phil Thornalley

CHORUS

178

I'm— al - rea - dy torn.——

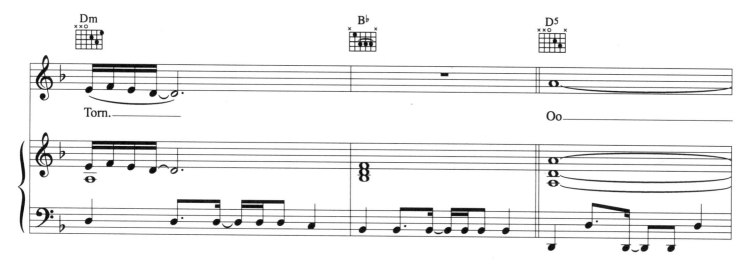

Torn.——

Oo——

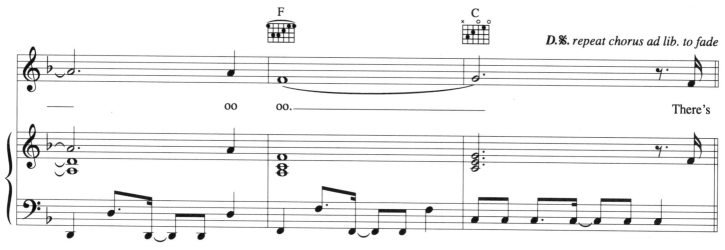

oo oo.——

There's

Final chorus:
I'm all out of faith
This is how I feel
I'm cold and I'm ashamed
Bound and broken on the floor.
You're a little late
I'm already torn…
Torn…

Think Twice

Words & Music by Andy Hill & Pete Sinfield

1. Don't think I can't feel that there's some-thing wrong,—
(Verse 2 see block lyric)

you've been the sweet-est part— of my life for so long.

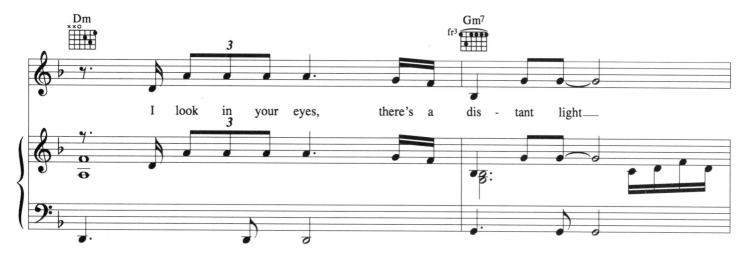

I look in your eyes, there's a dis - tant light___

and you and I know there'll be a storm to - night.___

This is get - ting ser - i - ous,

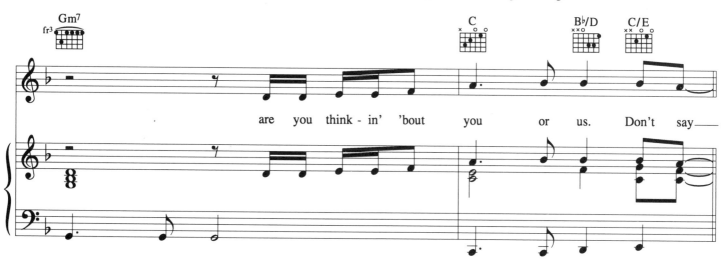

are you think - in' 'bout you or us. Don't say___

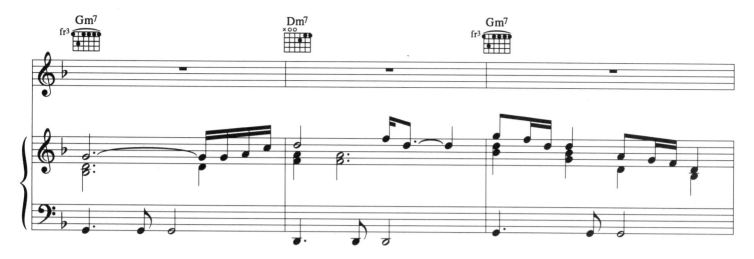

Ba - by this is ser - i - ous, are you think-in' a-bout

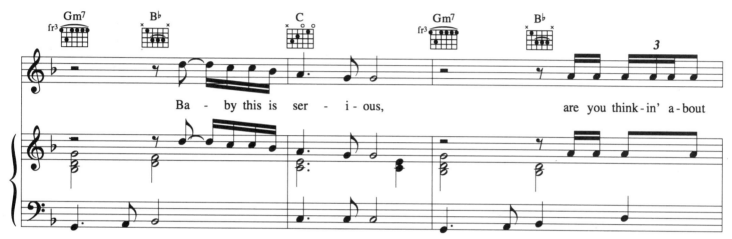

you___ or us?___ Ba - by.___ Don't say___

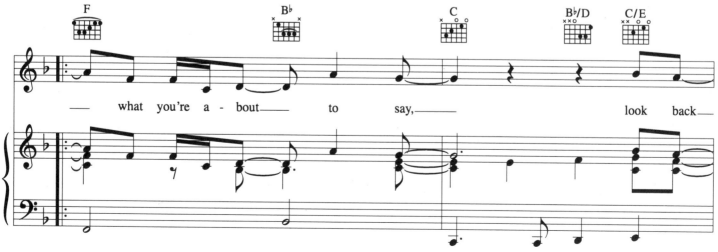

___ what you're a - bout___ to say,___ look back___

be - fore you leave my life. Be sure___

be - fore you close that___ door,___ be - fore you roll___

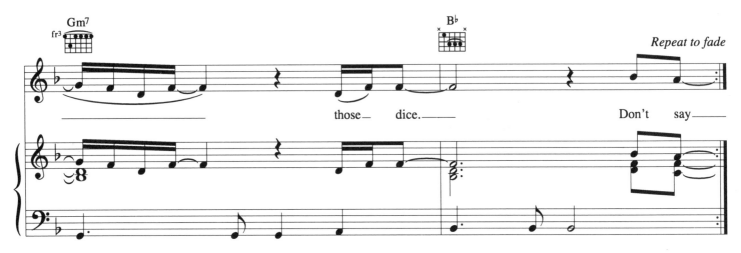

Repeat to fade

those— dice.___ Don't say___

Verse 2:
Baby think twice, for the sake of our love
For the memory,
For the fire and the faith
That was you and me.
Babe I know it ain't easy
When your soul cries out for higher ground,
'Cause when you're halfway up
You're always halfway down.

But baby this is serious
Are you thinking 'bout you or us?

Unchain My Heart

Words & Music by Freddy James & Bobby Sharp

Unchained Melody

Words by Hy Zaret
Music by Alex North

Wannabe

**Words & Music by Matt Rowe, Richard Stannard,
Melanie Brown, Victoria Aadams, Geri Halliwell, Emma Bunton & Melanie Chisholm**

♩=116

Yo I'll tell you what I want, what I real-ly real-ly want, so

tell me what you want, what you real-ly real-ly want. I'll

tell you what I want, what I real-ly real-ly want, so

tell me what you want, what you real-ly real-ly want. I wan-na,

tell you what I want, what I real-ly real-ly want, so

tell me what you want, what you real-ly real-ly want. I wan-na,

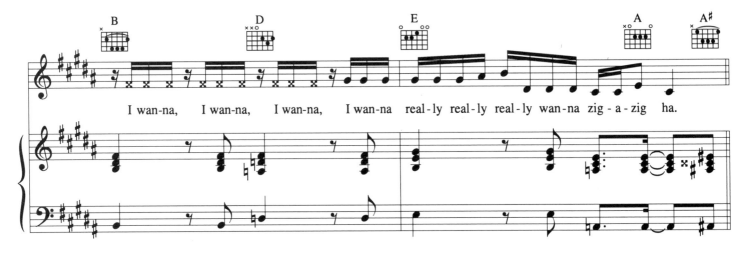

I wan-na, I wan-na, I wan-na, I wan-na real-ly real-ly real-ly wan-na zig-a-zig ha.

If you wan-na be my lov-er, you got-ta get with my friends.

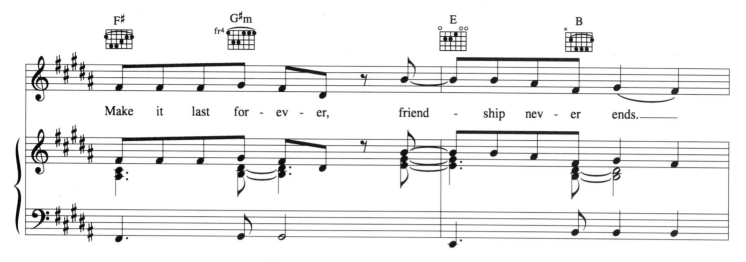

Make it last for - ev - er, friend - ship nev - er ends.___

If you wan - na be my lov - er, you have got to give,

1, 3. *To Coda ⊕*

tak - ing is too ea - sy, but that's___ the way it is.___

2.

(2° vocal ad lib.)

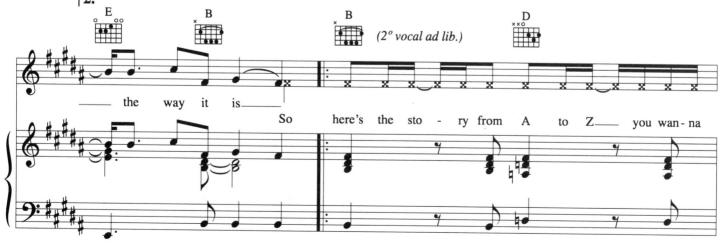

___ the way it is___ So here's the sto - ry from A to Z___ you wan - na

get with me,— you got-ta lis-ten care-ful-ly. You got M. in the place who likes— it in your face, you got

1.

G. like M. C. who likes— it on an ea - sy beat.

2.

D.℁. al Coda
(repeat chorus)

ev-'ry-bo-dy down and wind— it all a-round.

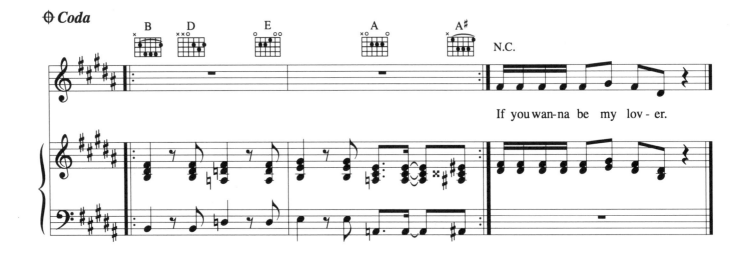

⊕ Coda

If you wan-na be my lov - er.

Verse 2:
What do you think about that now you know how I feel
Say you can handle my love, are you for real?
I won't be hasty, I'll give you a try
If you really bug me then I'll say goodbye.

Without You

Words & Music by Peter Ham & Tom Evans

give, I can't give a - ny - more._____ No, I

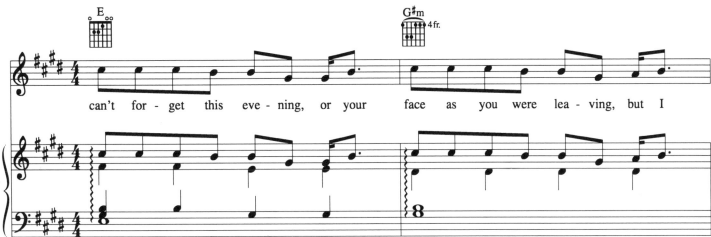

can't for - get this eve - ning, or your face as you were lea - ving, but I

guess that's just the way the sto - ry goes. You al - ways smile, but in your eyes your sor - row

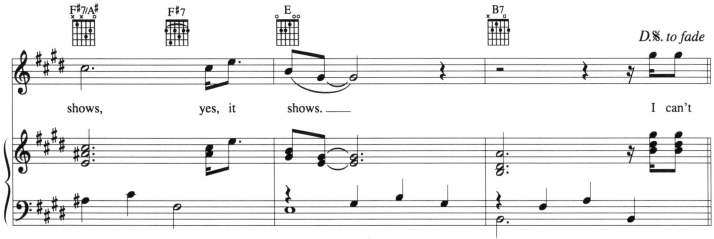

shows, yes, it shows.____ I can't

Wonderful Tonight

Words & Music by Eric Clapton

1. It's late in the eve - ning,
2. We go to a par - ty,
3. It's time to go home now,

she's won-d'ring what clothes to wear.
and ev - 'ry - one turns to see
and I've got an ach - ing head.

She puts on her make -
this beau - ti - ful la -
So I give her the car

I feel won-der-ful __ be-cause I see __ the love __ light in __ your

eyes. Then the won-der of it all __ is that you

just don't __ re - a - lise __ how much __ I love __ you.

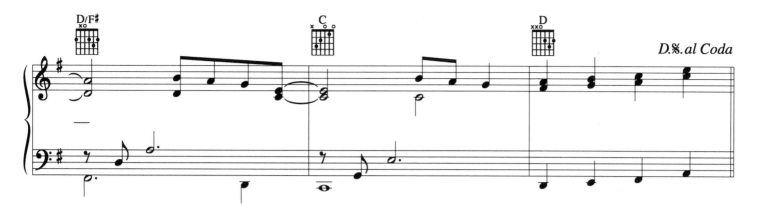

D.%.al Coda

⊕ Coda

Oh, my dar-ling, you are

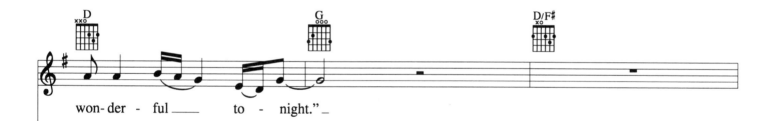

won-der-ful ___ to - night." _

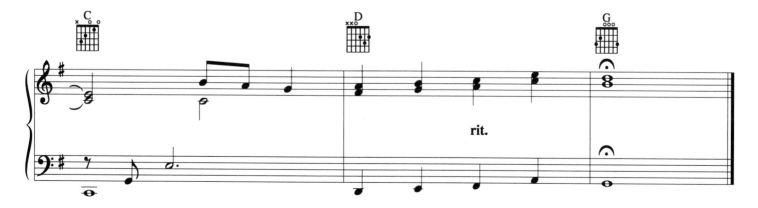

rit.

Wonderwall

Words & Music by Noel Gallagher

To-day is gon-na be the day that they're gon-na throw it back to you,—

by now you should-'ve some-how re-al-ised what you got-ta do.—

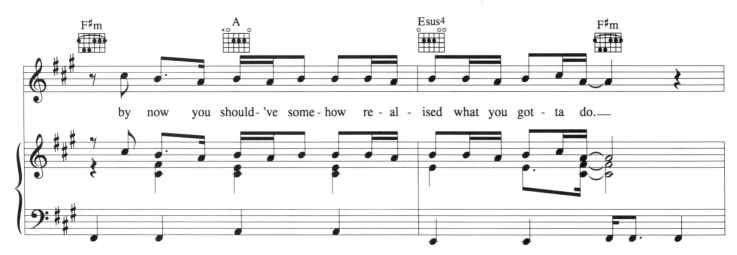

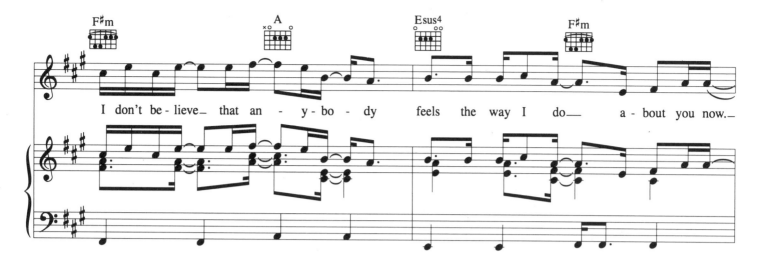

I don't be-lieve— that an-y-bo-dy feels the way I do— a-bout you now.—

1. Back-beat the word was on the street that the fi-re in your heart is out.—
(Verse 2 see block lyric)

I'm sure you've heard it all be-fore but you nev-er real-ly had a doubt.—

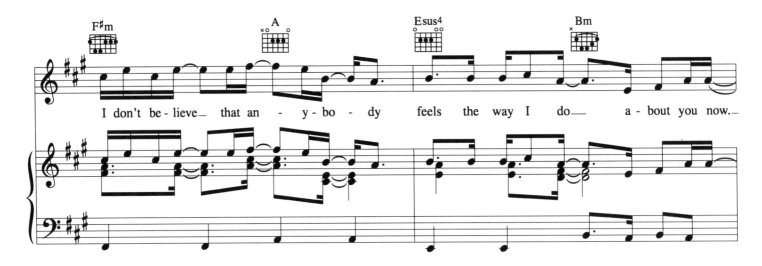

I don't be-lieve that an-y-bo-dy feels the way I do a-bout you now.

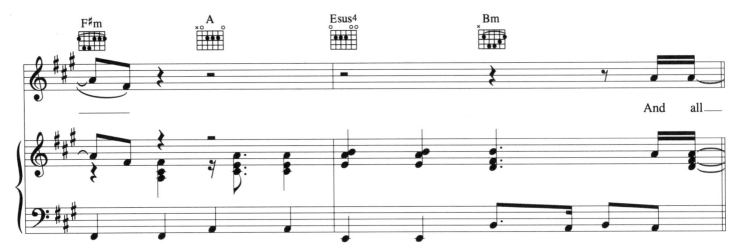

And all

the roads we have to walk are wind-ing and all

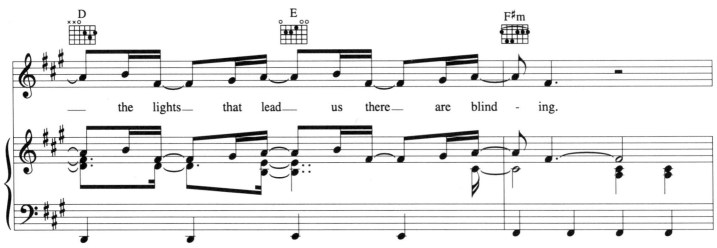

the lights that lead us there are blind-ing.

There are ma-ny things__ that I__ would like to say to you__ but I don't know how,—

{ be - cause }
{ I said }

may - be__   you're gon - na be the one that

saves me,—   and af - ter all_____

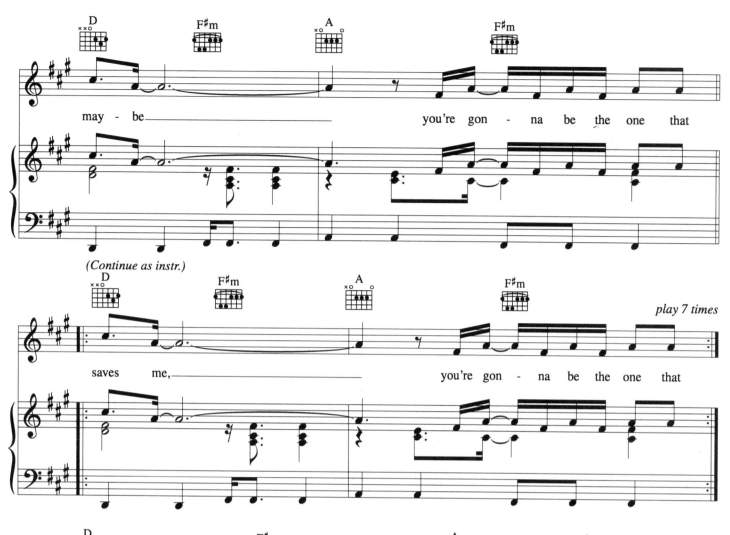

may - be_____ you're gon - na be the one that

(Continue as instr.)

play 7 times

saves me,_____ you're gon - na be the one that

Verse 2:
Today was gonna be the day
But they'll never throw it back to you
By now you should've somehow
Realised what you're not to do
I don't believe that anybody
Feels the way I do
About you now.

And all the roads that lead you there were winding
And all the lights that light the way are blinding
There are many things that I would like to say to you
But I don't know how.

Words

Words & Music by Barry Gibb, Robin Gibb & Maurice Gibb

gone   'cause that would bring a   tear   to me.   This

world   has   lost   its   glo - ry;   let's start a brand - new   sto - ry

now,   my   love.   Right now,   there'll be   no   oth - er

time,   and   I   can show you   how,   my   love. ___

Talk in ev-er-last-ing words and ded-i-cate them all to me.

And I will give you all my life, I'm here if you should

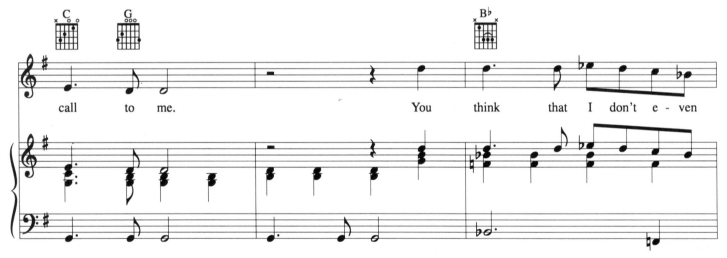

call to me. You think that I don't e-ven

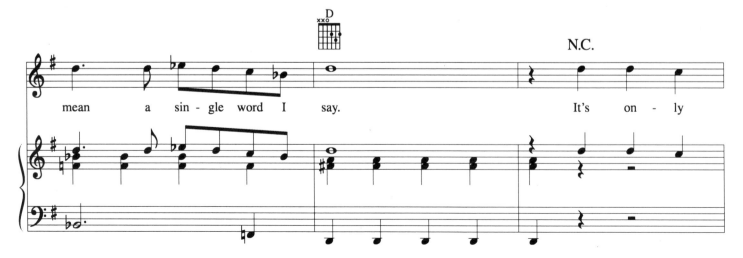

mean a sin-gle word I say. It's on-ly

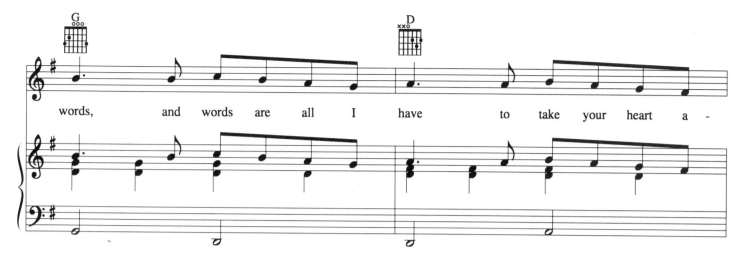

words,   and words are all I have   to take your heart a –

way.   It's on – ly words,   and words are all I

have   to take your heart a – way.   It's on – ly

words,   and words are all I have   to take your heart a – way.

rit.

You Can Call Me Al

Words & Music by Paul Simon

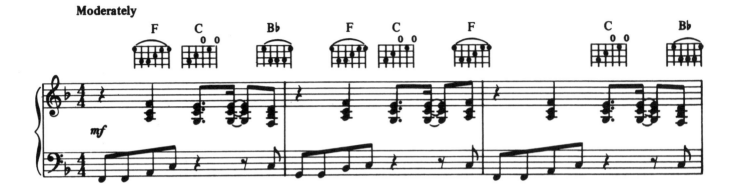

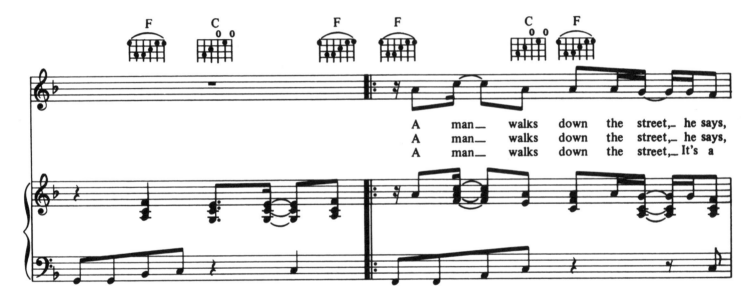

A man— walks down the street,— he says,
A man— walks down the street,— he says,
A man— walks down the street,— It's a

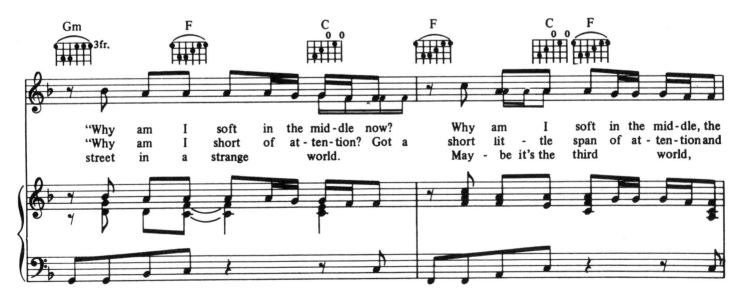

"Why am I soft in the mid-dle now?
"Why am I short of at-ten-tion? Got a
street in a strange world.

Why am I soft in the mid-dle, the
short lit-tle span of at-ten-tion and
May - be it's the third world,

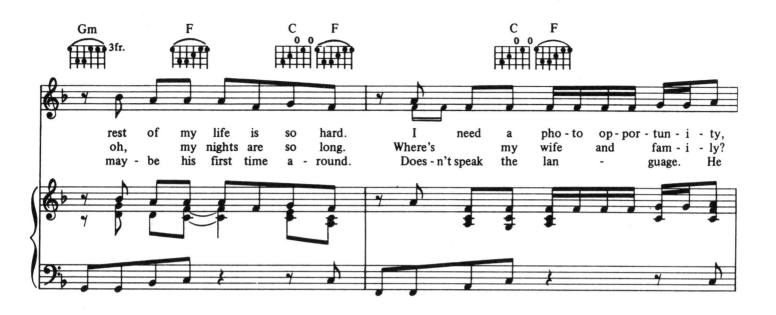

rest of my life is so hard.   I need a pho-to op-por-tun-i-ty,
oh, my nights are so long. Where's my wife and fam-i-ly?
may-be his first time a-round. Does-n't speak the lan - guage. He

I want a shot at re-demp-tion. Don't want to end up a car-toon in a
What if I die here? Who'll be my role mod-el
holds no cur-ren-cy. He is a for-eign man.

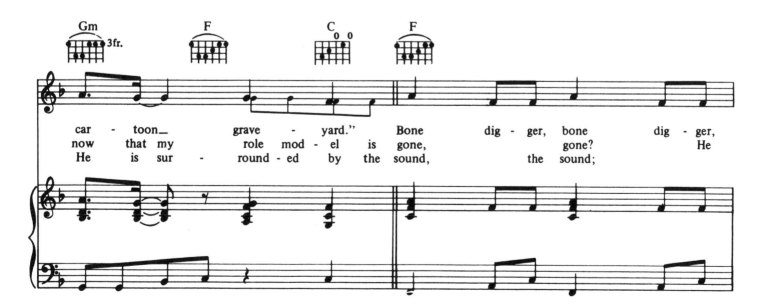

car - toon__ grave - yard." Bone dig - ger, bone dig - ger,
now that my role mod - el is gone, gone? He
He is sur - round - ed by the sound, the sound;

dogs in the moon - light___ far a - way in my well-lit door.___ Mis - ter
ducked back down the al - ley with some ro - ly po - ly lit - tle bat-faced girl.___ All a -
cat - tle in the mar - ket place,___ scat - ter - ings and or - phan-ag - es. He looks a -

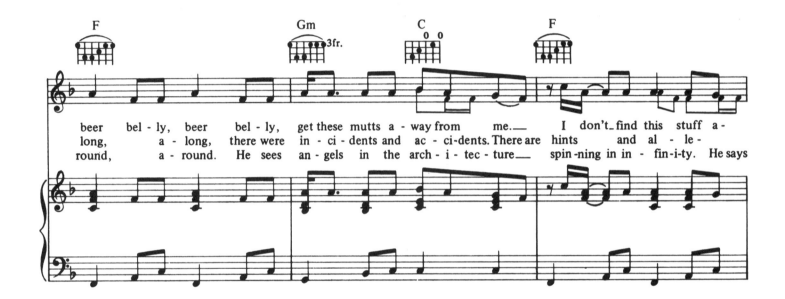

beer bel - ly, beer bel - ly, get these mutts a - way from me.___ I don't_ find this stuff a -
long, a - long, there were in - ci - dents and ac - ci - dents. There are hints and al - le -
round, a - round. He sees an - gels in the arch - i - tec - ture___ spin-ning in in - fin-i-ty. He says

mus - ing an - y - more.
ga - tions.
a - men and hal - le - lu - jah.   If you'll be my bod - y - guard___ I can be your long___ lost___

pal.

I can call you Bet - ty and

To Coda ⊕ 1.

Bet - ty, when you call me, you can   call me Al.

2.

Tacet

call   me   Al.___   Call   me Al.

D.C. al Coda ⊕

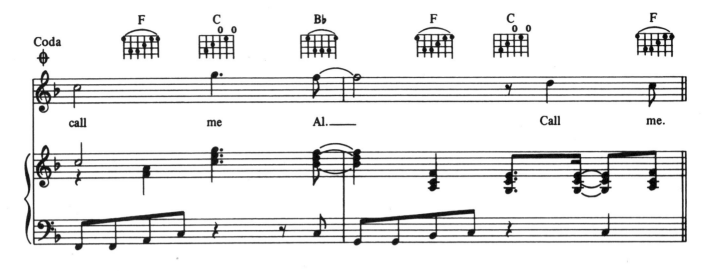

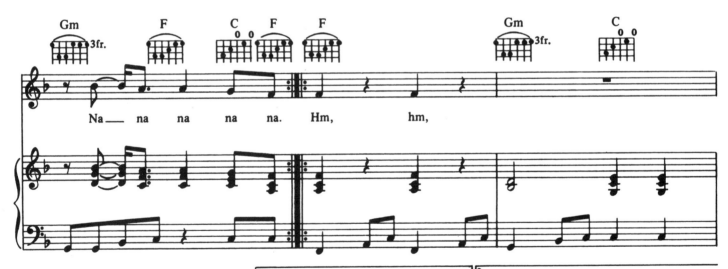

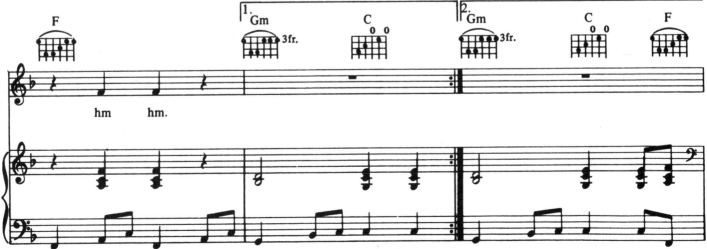

Tacet

Repeat and fade

If you'll be my bod - y - guard
I can call you Bet - ty.

Yesterday

Words & Music by John Lennon & Paul McCartney

Moderately, with expression

1. Yes - ter - day, ____ all my trou - bles seemed so
2. Sud - den - ly, ____ I'm not half the man ____ I

far a - way, Now it looks as though ____ they're
used to be, There's a shad - ow hang - ing

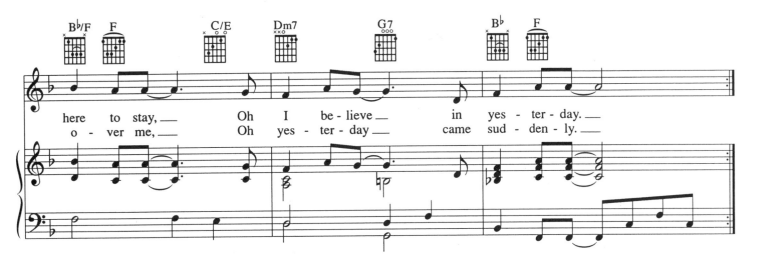

here to stay, ___ Oh I be - lieve ___ in yes - ter - day. ___
o - ver me, ___ Oh yes - ter - day ___ came sud - den - ly. ___

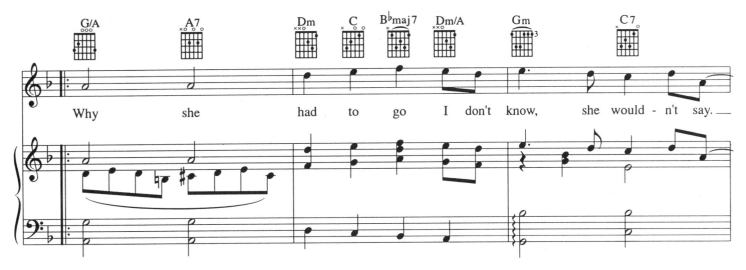

Why she had to go I don't know, she would - n't say. ___

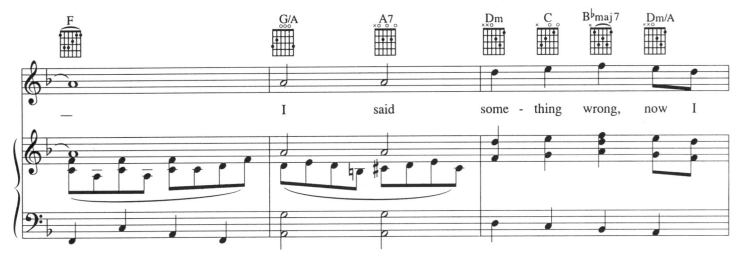

I said some - thing wrong, now I

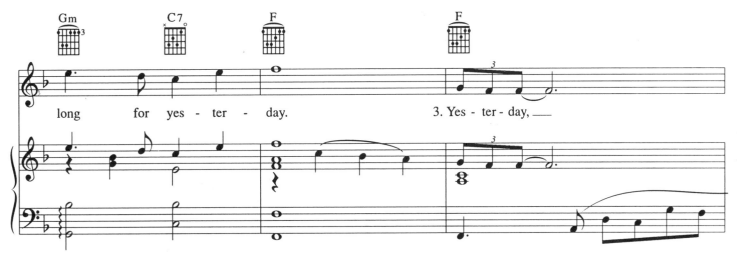

long for yes - ter - day. 3. Yes - ter - day, ___

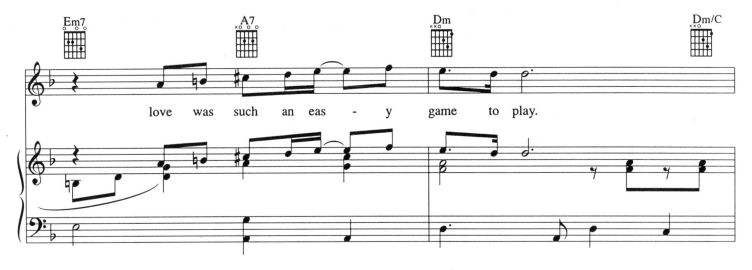

love was such an eas - y game to play.

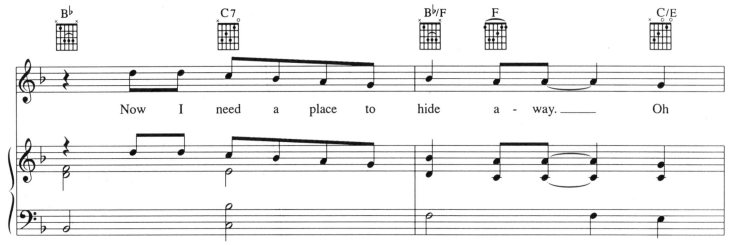

Now I need a place to hide a - way. _____ Oh

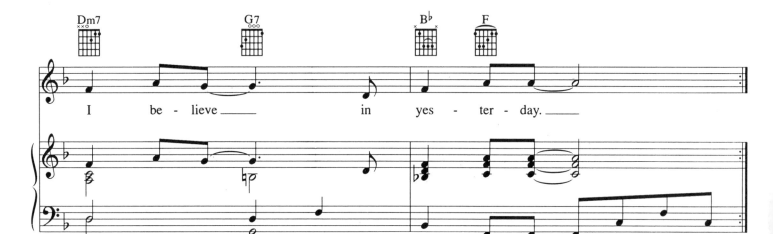

I be - lieve _____ in yes - ter - day. _____

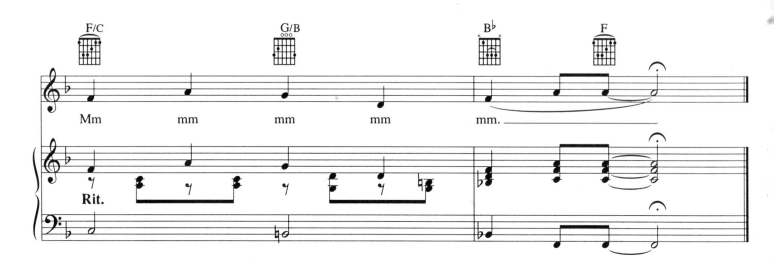

Mm mm mm mm mm. _____

Rit.

7/00(37535)